# EYƎ TRICKS

ISBN: 978-1-86200-490-0

10 9 8 7 6 5 4 3 2 1

## Bibliography

From the same authors:
*Puzzillusions*, Carlton Books Ltd, London, 2007
*Big Book of Optical Illusions*, Barron's Educational Series, New York, 2006
*Fantastic Optical Illusions*, Carlton Books Ltd, London, 2006
*MateMagica*, La Meridiana, Molfetta, Italy, 2005
*New Optical Illusions*, Carlton Books Ltd, London, 2005,
*Dazzling Optical Illusions*, Sterling Books, New York, 2002
*L'Almanach du mathematicien en herbe*, Editions Archimède, Paris, 2002
Other authors:
*Art and Visual Perception: A Psychology of the Creative Eye*, Rudolf Arnheim, University of California Press, 2004,
*The Science of Illusions*, Jacques Ninio, Cornell University Press, 2001, ISBN 0801437709
*Can You Believe Your Eyes?*, J. Block and R. Yuker, Routledge, 1989, ISBN 0876306954

## Credits

Page 94, Book cover, Aleksandr Rodchenko.
Page 101, Painting, Norman Parker.
Page 102, TSP art, Craig S. Kaplan.
Page 124, Sculptures, Guido Moretti.
Page 152, Photo, Mark Chester.

Printed in Dubai

# EYƎ TЯICKS

## More than 150 deceptive images, visual tricks and optical puzzlers

**Gianni A. Sarcone and Marie-Jo Waeber,**

**www.archimedes-lab.org**

SEVENOAKS

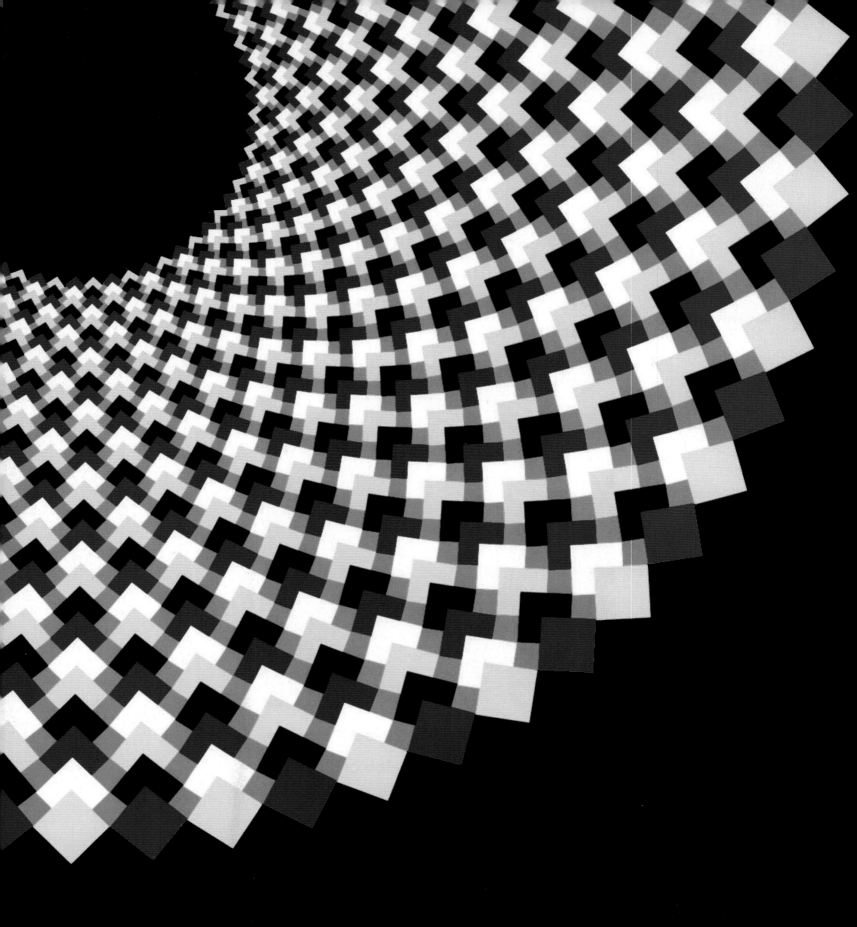

# Contents

# Foreword

'**Listen with your eyes.
See with your ears.**'

– Zen koan

'**Architects are taught to
privilege the visual and be
seduced by images. But we
live in all five of our senses...**'

– Hillary Brown

## A window on the world

Human beings are sponges who absorb changes in the physical world around them. Actually, if the physical world really were unchanging, there would be no point in us processing the sensations generated by the world that surrounds us since everything would be static anyway!

Our sense organs continuously check, then, the changes in our immediate environment to allow us to act and react accordingly. If we see a wall in front of us, for example, of course we don't charge into it, we try to avoid it. Our senses, however, detect only a part of the reality – the most useful for us – and translate it in an 'analogical' way. Yes, our senses work analogically... For instance, it's difficult to consider a single color in isolation. Rather, we always consider it in relation to other colors. The same red color will be perceived differently according to the context within which it lies.

Every living creature has a 'repertoire' of sense organs that is peculiar to him, with a particular predilection for one or two sense organs; the human being favors sight, the dog smell; for bats it's hearing… Animals don't all see color in the same way, because they don't all perceive the same part of the luminous spectrum. Here are two extreme examples: insects see ultraviolet rays, while some snakes can perceive infrared rays.

However, interpreting what our senses perceive is not an innate ability; our brain has to learn to decode the steady stream of sensorial information (the stimuli) in order to transform it into something 'comprehensible'. People born blind but who acquire their sight do not immediately understand what they see and have to face up to a long period of rehabilitation and discouragement before they become accustomed to seeing in the same way as everybody else.

I've always been fascinated and impressed by how people with partial or total visual sensory deficiencies interact with the world. We cannot talk about visual perception or optical illusions without mentioning the other side of the coin. To understand how these people 'see' without sight is to understand just how important our sense of sight is (unfortunately, sometimes we don't do it justice or give it the importance it deserves), and how it collaborates and integrates with the other sense organs. Have you ever asked yourself what it is when we see, walk, speak, feel and touch all at the same time; what links our sight with the sense of touch or hearing?

The reality is we actually see very little: only that on which we are concentrating or which we find important. Man without the crutches of the other sense organs would truly be lost, because it is these which permit us, subconsciously, to go about our everyday lives. A famous experiment demonstrated how at times we are really 'blind' in the truest sense of the word. In this experiment on 'inattentional blindness', performed in 1999, Daniel Simons and Christopher Chabris asked people to watch a video clip and count the number of times one of two teams of basketball players took

possession of the ball. Many people (around 40 per cent) just didn't notice a man in a gorilla suit entering stage right, doing a jig in the center of the screen and then leaving stage left. The clip demonstrated that we don't see what we don't pay attention to, even when it's in front of our eyes!

In this book we'll speak about one of the most highly prized sensorial organs of human beings, sight, by showing you, in an entertaining way, how the brain sometimes lets us be fooled by the world of images. Finally, we also want this book to stimulate thought about visual perception by referring to certain perception deficiencies, such as colorblindness and deaf-blindness, and offering you a couple of experiences which will allow you to better understand how people with these deficiencies perceive the world and communicate with us.

For me, Helen Keller remains the most iconic and inspirational figure. A severe fever at the age of 19 months left her blind and deaf, barely able to communicate, but Keller became an excellent student and eventually attended Radcliffe College, from which she graduated with honors in 1904! We simply couldn't speak about visual perception and visual illusions without mentioning those people who, through other organ senses, can 'see' and interact with their immediate environment, and it is to them that we dedicate this book.

## Gianni A. Sarcone
Designer and co-founder of Archimedes-lab.org

# Introduction

## What is an illusion?

We have five main senses – sight, hearing, taste, touch and smell – but about 75 per cent of the information humans receive about our environment comes from our sight, making it the most 'important' of the five senses. Vision depends, obviously, on the EYES to see (with optic receptors called rods and cones) and on the BRAIN to make sense of what we see. The optic nerve at the back of the eye connects to the central nervous system in the brain. The brain receives electrical impulses (stimuli) from our eyes, which are interpreted as SIGHT, but the brain adds two extra ingredients to the received image: memory and interpretation (in short, perception). Sometimes the brain is deceived by information received from the eyes. Visual illusions are caused when differences occur between our perceptions or expectations and the image seen by the eye. In fact, there are particular illusions which deceive the human visual system into perceiving something that is not present or incorrectly perceiving what is present.

Optical illusions can be roughly categorized as physical illusions, physiological illusions and cognitive illusions. Physical illusions are phenomenal illusions which occur before light enters the eye, such as a mirage or a rainbow... Physiological illusions are the effects on the eyes or brain of prolonged stimulation of a specific type, such as brightness, tilt, color, movement... Visual cognitive illusions interact with different levels of perceptual processing and inbuilt assumptions or 'knowledge' become misdirected. When we experience a visual cognitive illusion, the perceptual error remains compelling even when we are fully aware of its nature. In this case, awareness of the perceptual error by itself does not produce a more accurate perception. These kinds of illusions are, hence, exceedingly difficult to overcome! Cognitive illusions are commonly divided into ambiguous illusions, distorting illusions and paradoxical illusions.

So if visual illusions have existed since the dawn of time, what is the oldest optical illusion created by man? Perhaps it was performed by the first prehistoric woman when she put on make-up... But – joking aside – it can easily be reasoned that the concept of optical illusion is as old as man himself. Notwithstanding the lack of any written trace, the first human beings would certainly have noticed optical phenomena such as mirages, the size of the Moon at its zenith, sticks or poles which appear to be broken in two when half-immersed in water, a negative image after having looked at the sun… One of the first optical illusions (or ambiguous images) knowingly created by man is from 2,500 years ago. On certain coins from the island of Lesbos, Greece, you can see the profiles of two animals facing each other. They are apparently herbivores such as cows or goats, which, however, form a third animal – a ferocious animal, maybe a wolf – when seen from the front. More recently, great names from art – Arcimboldo, René Magritte, Salvador Dalí and many others – have utilized optical illusions for artistic ends.

**Expanding disc**
*Due to the PDI effect (see page 13), this hypnotic geometric pattern seems to expand slightly.*

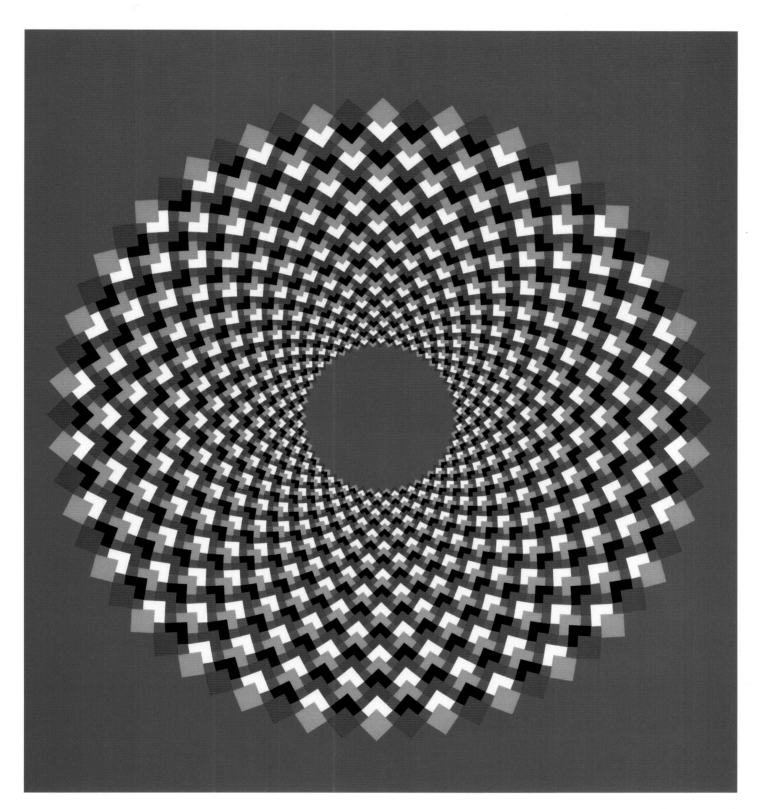

**Color spiral**
*The color vortex appears to draw your gaze up to its center.*

Most of the optical illusions featured in this book were invented by Gianni A. Sarcone and Marie-Jo Waeber, the authors. However, in the following pages you will also be delighted by some uncommon or new visual curiosities created by other emerging or notable talented artists.

So in this book various classic and new optical illusions are depicted, covering: ambiguous and completion figures, impossible figures, hidden objects, illusions involving colors, geometric illusions, illusory moving patterns, verbal illusions and paradoxes. All these illusions were designed by the authors with the aim of allowing the reader to

- discover how we perceive things
- test and enhance his powers of observation and critical thinking skills
- improve his mental flexibility
- have fun being deceived by puzzling visual challenges.

# 'One's own view of reality as the only reality is the most dangerous of all delusions.'

— Paul Watzlawick

## Images are tricky

This book is not just to 'look at'. We are sure, however, that you bought it (at least, we hope you bought it – the store detectives were filming you!) because you like amusing yourself with visual puzzles. Recognizing a hidden figure by turning the book around, guessing a visual word game, or cutting out and rearranging figures are all wonderful things you can do while sitting in a comfy armchair with your pipe and slippers, or even when you're having a good time with your friends in a bar (although the puzzles might become a little harder after a certain length of time…!)

What we are also interested in, though, with our entertaining visual games and illusions, is to make you reflect upon (and experience) the intrinsic power of the images. As many people have said, a picture paints a thousand words; the persuasive power of images is so strong that they can lead you astray and can even be used as instruments of propaganda. Here is a small example of this, but it's one that we like very much…

On an island, a long way from anywhere, the people practiced cannibalism. After many years, thanks to the assiduous work of missionaries (and after much active participation in the native cuisine), this horrible habit was lost. Instead, food stores were opened by various multinationals. Products arrived from all over the world: typical tinned products such as meat, vegetables, fish etc. After a while, the local authorities became worried when a certain brand of tinned meat with the picture of a chubby-cheeked baby began selling like hot cakes. We are sure you have worked out why… For most of us the image of a person licking their fingers on a tin of meat would mean that the meat inside was delicious, but for the natives of the island, having not long left behind their isolation (and cannibalism), the image represented the flesh of a very fat and tasty baby. As you can see, the significance of an image depends distinctly on our cultural background and personal experiences.

The greatest optical illusion is to believe that an image has only one interpretation! There is little or no questioning of the conventional uses of images and often photographs are treated as transparent windows on what they are meant to represent – with the risk of producing, as you have just seen, a diametrically opposite meaning!

Try this experiment. Scan a photo of yourself and, with the help of photo retouching software, flip it horizontally to create a mirror image. Print it out and compare this image with the original photo. Which of the two faces do you prefer? Show both images to a friend and ask which version he prefers. You will probably prefer the mirror image and your friend the 'normal' version. It's a question of habit; we prefer that which we are used to. Two visions of the same person!

As you can see, behind every image we perceive there is another that we haven't seen, but which others have, and vice versa. To learn to read images in an objective manner would be a great step forward for human beings. In fact, we live submersed in images and visual communication acquires more importance and power every day. Knowing how to use visual language for the best helps us to communicate better, enriching our palette of expression. But to believe in the objectivity of images, alas, is just a dream. As Charlie Chaplin said, 'The performing act is a creation of misunderstanding.' Substituting 'image' for 'performing act', we summarize rather well the value of images.

Just like a good book on philosophy or psychology, optical illusions help us to reflect upon, and to understand a little better, some of the errors of perception we make every day. To learn how we 'read' the images and why we commit some perceptual errors is the goal of this book, but we won't neglect the anecdotal or amusing side!

## Some useful terms you will find in the book

**Camouflage** has been used for disguise in the natural world ever since predators developed eyes to track prey. In optical illusions, it is the art of hiding something elegantly in an image. Most often these are landscapes or natural scenes where extra animals or objects are hidden.

### Neon effect
*The white zones between the blue rays look bluish and the edge of the central yellow disc seems to shine.*

**Color contrast** (simultaneous) happens when:
**a.** colors shift their hues in the direction of the complementary color (the opposite effect of 'color assimilation', where colors tend to adopt similar hues).
**b.** colors look lighter or darker with respect to the background color (essentially the same effect as with black and white).
Simultaneous color contrast is related, and very similar, to 'simultaneous brightness contrast'.

**Color assimilation** is when the areas of color in a pattern subtend very small angles to the observer (less than about a third of a degree) an effect opposite to simultaneous contrast occurs; colors appear to become more like their neighbors instead of less like them.

**Hue induction** is when 'color contrast' and 'color assimilation' (see above) demonstrate that the perceived brightness/color of an object or region of a scene does not depend simply on its own brightness/color. There are basically two phenomena:
**a.** the same color may look different.
**b.** different colors may lead to a similar color impression.

**Inattentional blindness** is the inability to perceive features in a visual scene if they are not being attended to; that is to say, humans have a limited capacity for attention, which thus limits the amount of information they can process at any particular time. Any otherwise salient feature within the visual field will not be observed if not processed by attention. This inattentional blindness is closely related to 'change blindness'.

**Change blindness** is a phenomenon in visual perception where large changes within a visual scene are undetected by the viewer. Typically, for change blindness to occur the change in the scene has to coincide with some visual disruption, such as an eye movement

## Hidden lines
*Find five continuous straight lines in the drawing.*

which it was being viewed, so the RAF decided to fit an array of electric lights to their anti-submarine aircraft, along the leading edges of the flying surfaces and to the nose. The intensity of the lamps was variable and was adjusted to a level such that the apparent brightness of the aircraft matched the luminance of the background sky. With this system, the bombers were able to approach and attack the U-boats with greater success, although the technique rapidly became obsolete as radar came into common usage.

***Lateral inhibition*** is a visual perception mechanism which enhances the contrast of the outline of an object. It is called 'lateral inhibition' because each photo-receptor in our eye tends to inhibit the response of the one next to it. The result is that something which appears to be clear appears even more so, and vice versa. The same mechanism works for colors; when a photo-receptor from one area of the retina becomes stimulated by a color, those next to it become less sensitive to that color. So, for example, the light blue of a small square seen on a blue background appears to our eyes clearer than it would do on a yellow background (because yellow contains no blue).

***Lightness*** is the 'perceived' incident light reflected from a surface. It is a subjective attribute of the color known usually as 'shade' and is measured in grayscale, from black to white. It represents the visual system's attempt to determine the relative brightness of an object in comparison with the brightness of other objects in the scene.

***Luminance*** is a physical quantity that can be measured by physical devices and indicates how much luminous power will be perceived by an eye looking at the surface from a particular angle. Luminance is thus an indicator of the 'light intensity' of a surface (of how bright the surface will appear). It is used in the video industry to characterize the brightness of displays.

***Mach bands*** are an optical illusion named after the physicist Ernst Mach. The term refers to bands adjacent to a light-to-dark gradient which appear lighter or darker than is justified by the underlying light. The effect is one of increased, local, perceived brightness on either side of a luminance gradient. In other words, the Mach bands show the effect of contrast at a boundary; at the boundary of a lighter bar with a darker bar, the edge of the lighter bar looks darker than the rest of that bar, whereas the edge of the darker bar looks lighter than the rest of the darker bar. It is usually supposed that this effect is caused by lateral inhibition of the receptors in the eye.

or a brief obscuration of the observed scene or image. Studies have shown that change blindness occurs when the change is introduced during a cut or pan in a motion picture, even when the change is to the central actor in a scene. People also regularly fail to notice editing errors in commercial movies, despite the intense scrutiny to which movies are subjected during the production process.

***Isoluminance*** or ***equiluminance*** is a term used to describe two colors which are equally bright. Isoluminance was used during World War Two; RAF Coastal Command bomber crews could easily spot surfaced U-boats and would try to attack them, but the U-boat crews could just as easily see the bombers and would dive before the planes could successfully attack. The problem was that the aircraft was always a different shade from the background against

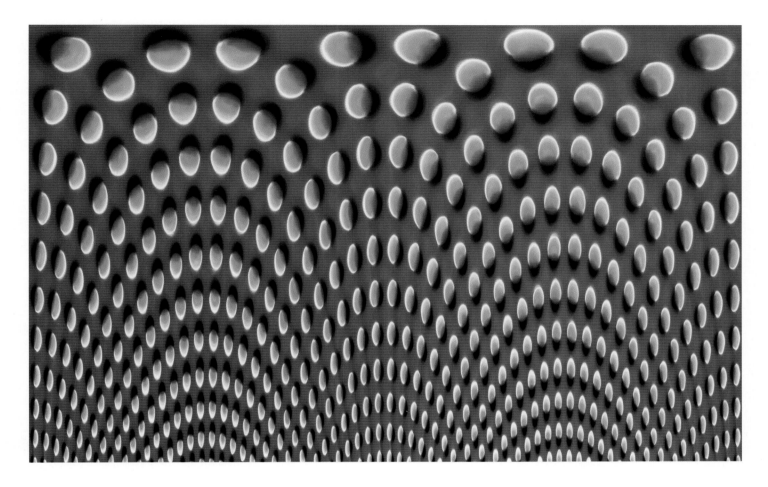

**Orientation contrast** (simultaneous) is an optical illusion in which a test line or shape surrounded by lines of a differing orientation changes its apparent orientation in a direction away from that of the surrounding lines. Orientation is a domain *sui generis*, in which simultaneous contrast occurs in the same manner as in the domains of color and brightness.

**Pareidolia**, a term first used in 1994 by Steven Goldstein, describes a kind of illusion or misperception in which something meaningless is considered meaningful. Common examples include images of animals or faces in clouds, the man in the moon and so on.

**Peripheral drift illusion (PDI)** refers to a motion illusion – also called 'anomalous motion' illusion – generated by the presentation of a sawtooth luminance grating (repeated contrasted patterns) in the visual periphery. The illusion is easily seen when fixating off to the side and then blinking as fast as possible. Most observers see the illusion easily when reading text

**It moves! (above)**
*A three-dimensional PDI effect... If you shift your gaze around the picture, the pearl-like shapes will begin to alternately ascend or descend. This visual illusion works better when observed under adequately lit conditions. Anomalous or apparent motion illusions are based on optical contrasts to create a visual perturbation. These kinds of compelling illusions were first described by the scientists A. Fraser and K. Wilcox.*

with the illusion figure in the periphery. The illusion is mainly due to the color contrast of the repeated patterns and to temporal differences in luminance processing producing a signal that tricks the motion system. Anomalous motion illusions work better on a computer screen (because of the luminance), so in order to appreciate better some of the PDI images contained in this book you can try scanning them and then looking at them on your PC.

# Gallery I

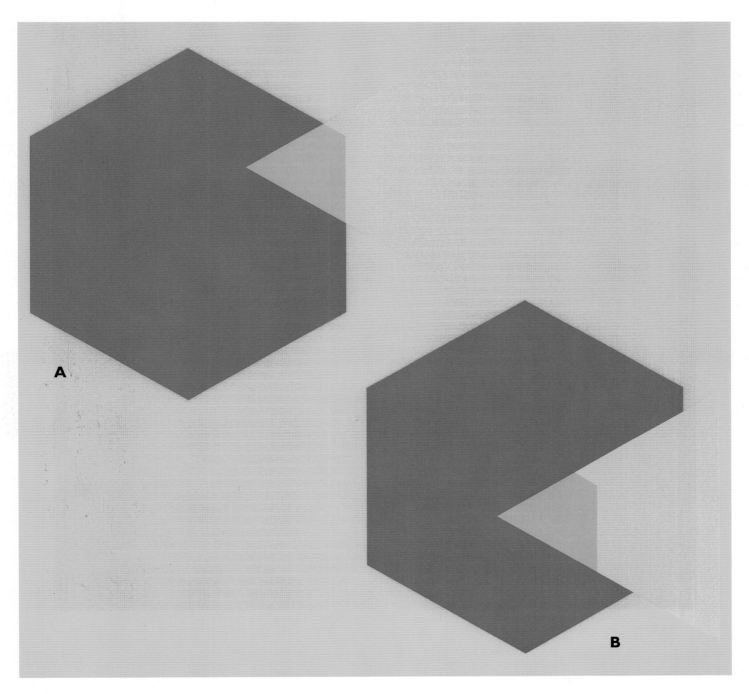

**Transparent vs opaque**
The green color within the triangular shape in fig. A seems slightly lighter than in fig. B. The difference of luminance is because the triangular shape in A is perceived as transparent, while the triangular shape in B is seen as opaque. There's a reason for this…
*See page 36*

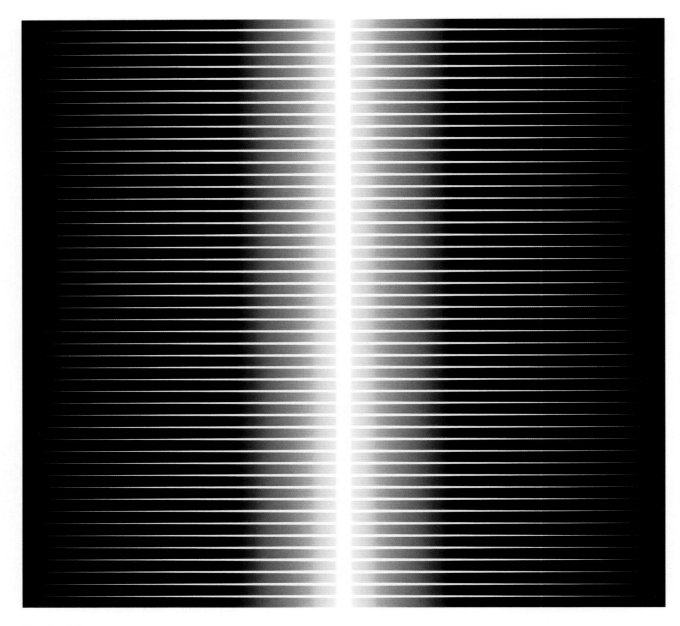

**Vertical flow**

The vertical line seems to glow. Actually, it appears much brighter than the surrounding white color of the page! You may also perceive within its center a thin line with some flowing movement of dark spots similar to the 'snow' effect on your TV.
*See page 36*

**Where is the boyfriend?**
Find the kissing cowgirl's boyfriend.
*See page 36*

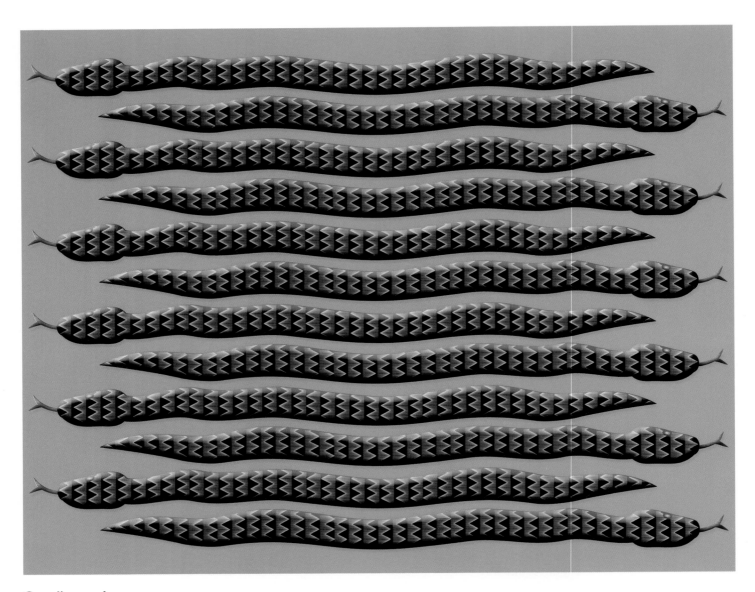

**Crawling snakes**

Observe the snakes in the picture for a while. Then move your gaze around the picture and the snakes will appear to move slightly.

*See page 36*

### Wash whiter than white

Recover the white color of Donald's plumage! As you can see, the left side of the photograph is bluish, while the right side has too much yellow. To restore the color balance, stare at the X in the second diagram for 20 to 30 seconds, then look at the duck again.
*See page 36*

**Count the squares!**
How many squares are there in the diagram? Look at the picture from
a distance. Do you perceive some vertical bands tinted in rose and
pistachio-green colors?
*See page 36*

**Where you bean?**
Find a child in the pile of coffee beans!
*See page 37*

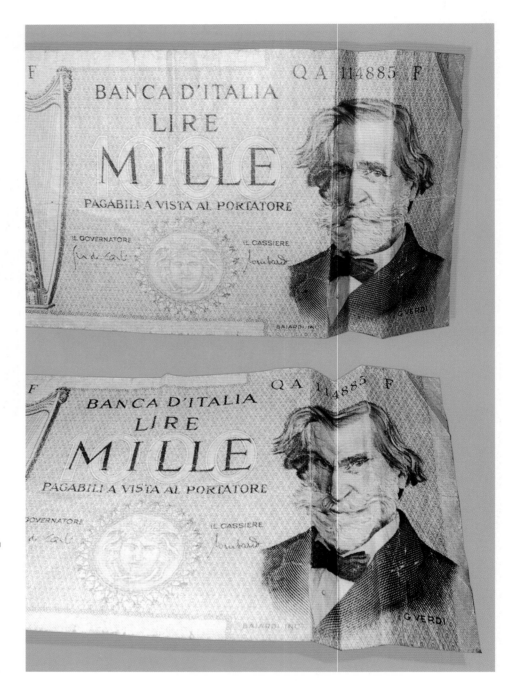

## Happy Verdi

Illusions with banknotes are very common in all countries. Here is an illusion with an old 1,000-lire bank note. By making hill-folds through the edges of Verdi's mouth and through his eyes, and then tilting the note back and forth, you can make the great composer appear happy or sad. You can perform this illusion using a British bank note featuring the Queen.

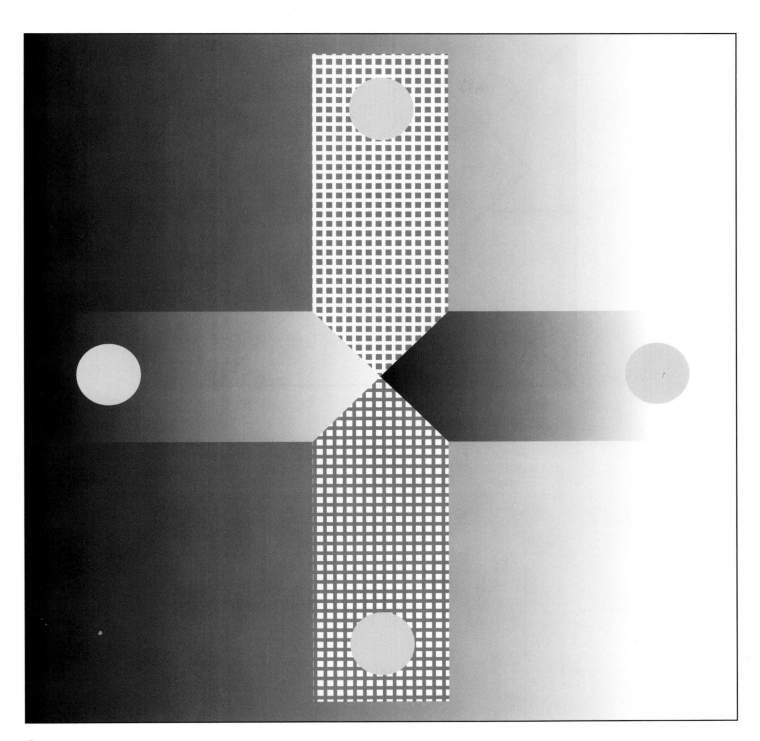

**Gray spots**
Are the four discs displayed on the bars of
the cross of the same color? Are you sure?
*See page 37*

**A**

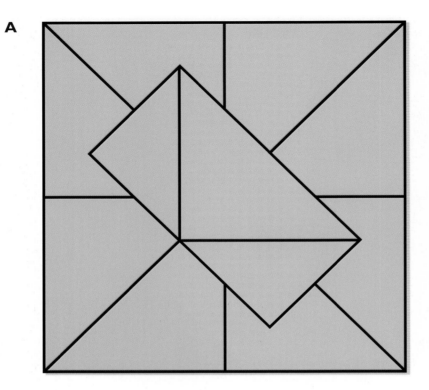

**B**

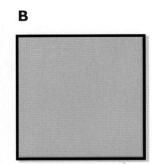

**Leonardo's puzzle**
Copy and cut out the 11-piece puzzle in fig. A.
Challenge 1: compose a square again by including square piece B.
Challenge 2: is it possible to form a perfect square with the 11-piece puzzle if its central right triangle is placed as shown in fig. C?
*See page 37*

**C**

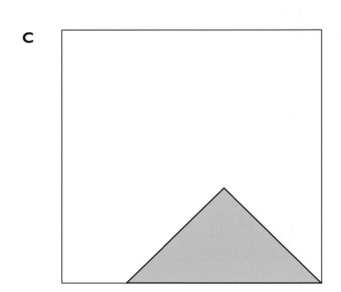

**Completion man**

Normal visual perception requires us to discriminate between foreground and background objects. However, in the picture, even though we can't see the body of the man, which is blended with the background (actually only the hands and the head are apparent), it appears complete. The tendency of our brain to complete a physical structure when it is only partially perceived is called amodal completion. Thanks to our prior perception experiences, we can make out a complete man.

**Dr Jekyll and Mr Hyde**
Do you see one or two faces, or can you
see all three? This kind of 'undecidable'
figure has been known since ancient times!

## Braille paradox

The Braille system, devised in 1821 by the French educator Louis Braille, is a method widely used by blind people to read and write. Each Braille character, or 'cell', is made up of arrangements of one to six raised dots representing letters and numerals, and can be identified by touch. Can you guess why the message in Braille on this page is a paradox?

*See page 37*

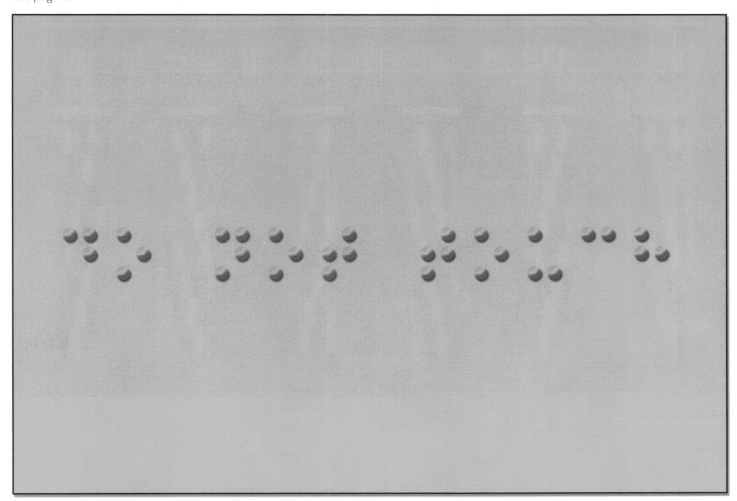

**Roman temple**
Do the columns of this Roman temple
converge (or diverge)? Veni, vidi and not vici…
*See page 37*

**Glasses experiment**
Is this image real or is it a photomontage?
*See page 37*

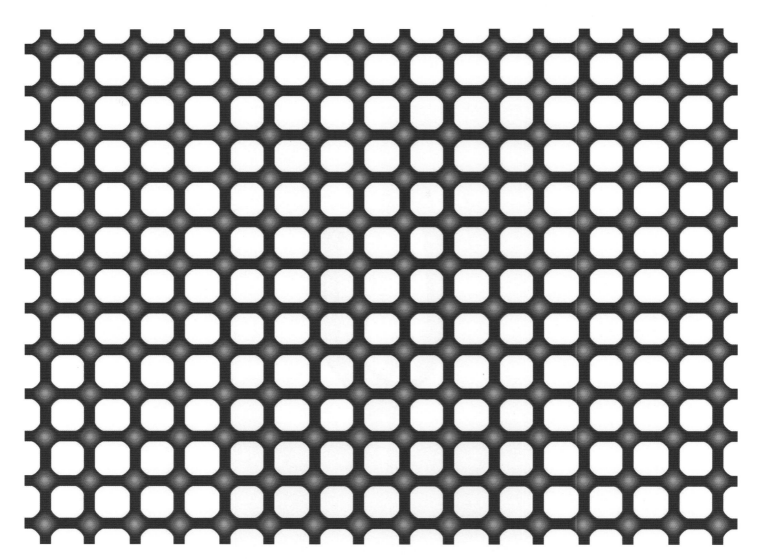

**Electric glance**

Shift your gaze around the picture representing an arrangement of lightbulbs. Groups of lightbulbs will then gradually appear to lose their intensity in the direction in which your gaze is pointed.

*See page 37*

**Gray colors**
Do the light gray triangular shapes
have the same brightness?
*See page 37*

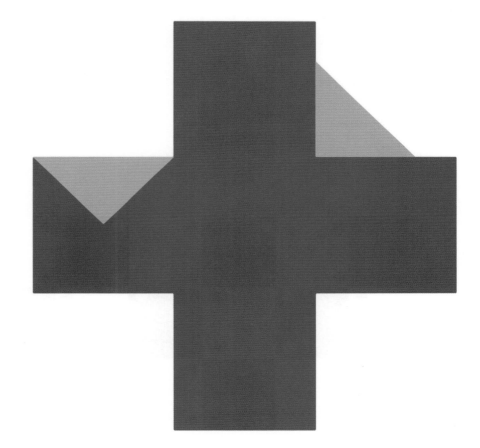

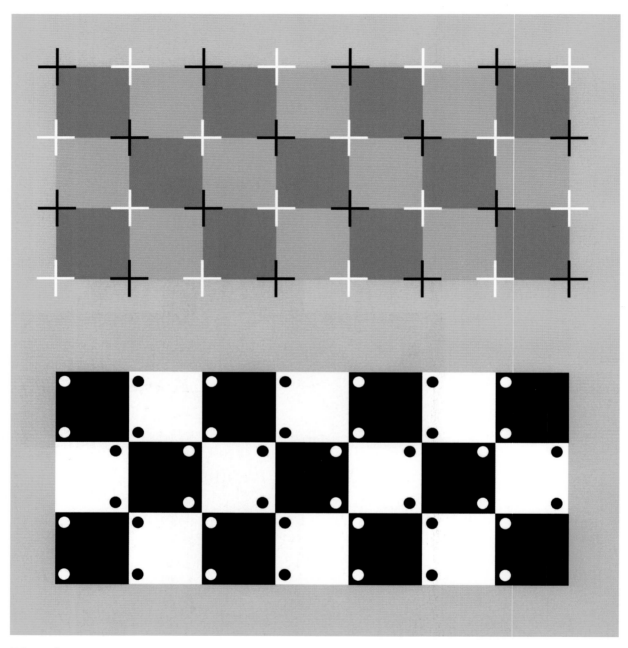

## Distortions

When you 'disturb' the edges of the squares which make up a checkered design with alternating small white and black regular shapes, as shown in the picture, the rows of the pattern may appear to tilt or diverge slightly.

Try to reproduce this optical effect by using a real checkerboard or a ready-to-use checkered pattern. Instead of crosses or dots you can draw lines, squares, rhombi, etc.

*See page 37*

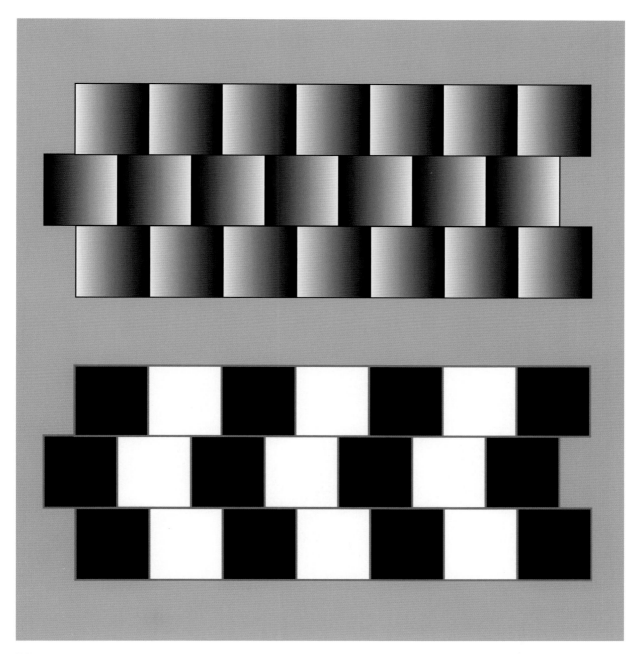

## Divergences

Tilting effects can be created with rows of squares having a hue gradation within them, or with alternating light and dark squares laid in staggered rows. It is essential for this illusion to work that each square is surrounded by a layer of 'mortar' (in gray in the image).

### Stubbs illusion

This illusion, based on the Stubbs illusion, involves
dynamic luminance-gradient effects. What happens
here? First, sit at a comfortable distance and then
move forward towards the center of the figure. A
change in apparent brightness — and, to some degree,
form — will result. By moving back and forth, this
apparent change will repeat. Interestingly, if you fix
your gaze steadily on the center of the image, the
black smudge also seems to expand slightly.
*See page 37*

**Levitating or not?**

This is an ambiguous picture. Do you see the shadow of the levitating vase or is it just a stain on the tablecloth? Who knows what's real!

# Gallery I Solutions

**Transparent vs opaque** (page 15)
A.: This effect of color scission is called the Metelli transparency effect. The Gestalt psychologist Fabio Metelli developed a theory about how the properties of the elements are split up in the transparency range. According to Metelli, the color properties of overlapping are governed by the proportional addition of color from the properties of the foreground and the opaque middle-ground.

**Vertical flow** (page 16)
This illusion is related to the illusory 'Mach bands' and results when gradients from darker to lighter shades are created.

**Where is the boyfriend?** (page 17)
Have a look at the large white spot on the head of the horse…

**Crawling snakes** (page 18)
These kinds of self-moving shapes are related to the peripheral drift illusion (PDI). The illusion is induced by the color contrast of the repeated patterns of the snakes' skin.

**Wash whiter than white** (page 19)
There are three main types of color receptors in the eye (red, green and blue) and by staring at one color for a long time you tire out those receptors, so when you look at the duck again the bluish and yellowish zones of the picture will be resorbed briefly because of the previous desensitization to blue and yellow, making the plumage of the duck appear uniformly white.

**Count the squares!** (page 20)

In the image we can perceive four different sets of squares (see picture): 6 × 6 large squares aligned diagonally, 7 × 7 small squares aligned diagonally, 6 × 6 large squares aligned orthogonally and 12 × 12 small squares aligned orthogonally. In total, there are in the picture 36 + 49 + 36 + 144 = 265 perfect squares! The illusory tinted bands are due to the 'watercolor illusion effect' which presents two main effects: a long-range assimilative color spreading (coloration effect) and properties imparting a strong figure status (figure-ground organization) to a region delimited by a dark (eg. purple) contour flanked by a lighter chromatic contour (eg. green).

## Where you bean? (page 21)

This kind of puzzle is called a hidden-figure puzzle. Generally they consist of a single image accompanied by a caption. The text, one or two lines long, introduces the image and indicates the object(s) to be found in the drawing. The image should then be turned in every direction to find the hiding place of the subject.

## Gray spots (page 23)

Yes, the discs are all of the same color. Seventy per cent of people given this test perceive three different hues within the discs: white (or light gray), medium gray and dark gray. The illusion is due to the brightness contrast.

## Leonardo's puzzle (page 24)

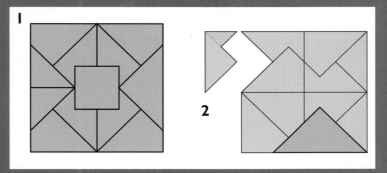

Challenge 1: see fig. 1. Challenge 2: it is possible to form a square only if you cut a small triangular shape from a piece of the puzzle, as shown in fig. 2.

## Braille paradox (page 27)

Because the message reads 'Do not touch', but if the blind person doesn't touch it, he can't know the instruction says not to touch it... and when he reads the Braille message with his fingers, it's too late. That's a paradox!

## Roman temple (page 28)

No, the columns of the temple are perfectly parallel. This interesting version of the Popple illusion shows how vertical bars, including an alignment of patterns adequately shifted, can induce a tilt sensation.

## Glasses experiment (page 29)

It's real. You can reproduce this installation by using two aligned glasses and a bright, bicolor background. You'll obtain the optical effect shown on the picture only when both glasses are FULL of water (or vodka, if you prefer).

## Electric glance (page 30)

This is a variation of the famous scintillating grid illusion by Lingelbach and the effect is mainly due to lateral inhibition of our visual system.

## Gray colors (page 31)

Believe it or not, both triangular surfaces possess the same luminance (brightness)! Despite having the same border contact with regions of higher and lower luminance, the right-hand triangle appears slightly darker, apparently at odds with an explanation in terms of color contrast. The Gestalt psychologists explain this difference by saying that one triangular shape appears to belong to the cross, while the other does not ('belongingness'). This illusion is called the Wertheimer-Benary cross, after the Gestalt psychologists who discovered it.

## Distortions (page 32)

An explanation of this phenomenon, which involves the contour and boundary perception of our visual system, is given in our previous books *New Optical Illusions* and *The Big Book of Optical Illusions*. Angles also play a role, directly or indirectly; the overestimation or underestimation of angles can result in what is referred to as a geometrical optical illusion.

## Stubbs illusion (page 34)

According to Alan Stubbs, the researcher who first noticed it, the change in apparent brightness is due to 'dynamic change from rod to cone vision and changes in neural functioning that accompany the changing visual angle at which the figure is viewed'.

# Gallery II

**Vertigo**
Stare at the center of this hypnotic image, representing a bird's eye view of a street between two skyscrapers. Does the middle of the street appear larger than its ends? Hey, don't lean forward too much!
See page 60

**Magic fluids**
If you concentrate on the
circular rings, you may perceive
a scattering, vibrating fluid.
Color contrasts are responsible
for such an optical effect.

**Distorted squares?**
Are both squares A and B distorted?
See page 60

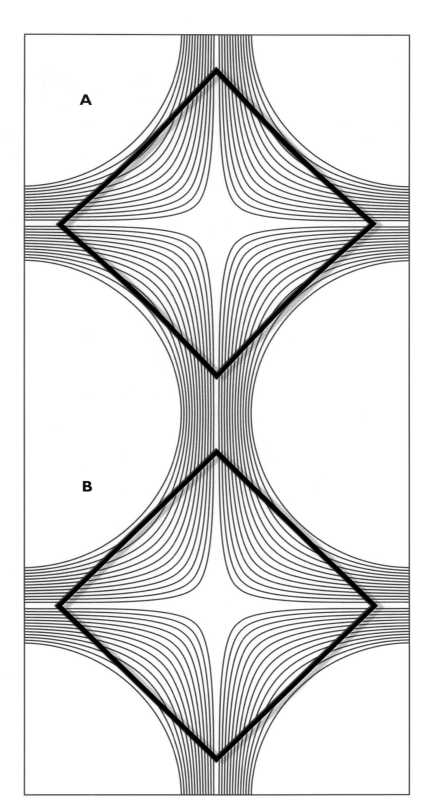

**Magnetic fields**

The 'magnetic' color fields of this drawing seem to vibrate when you move the page. If you move your head backwards and forwards keeping the focus on the disc at the center of the image, the color fields seem to bulge considerably! This illusion involves color contrast and dynamic luminance-gradient effects.

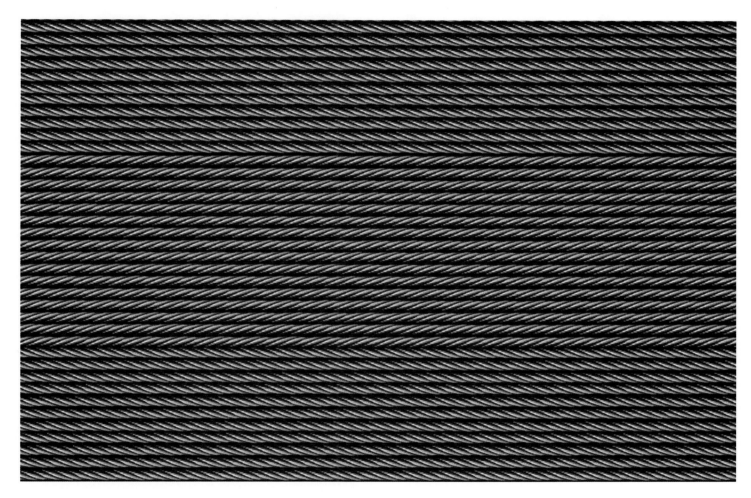

**Twisted steel ropes**
Are all the cables perfectly straight and
parallel? Take a magnifying glass and
examine the photo. What do you notice?
See page 60

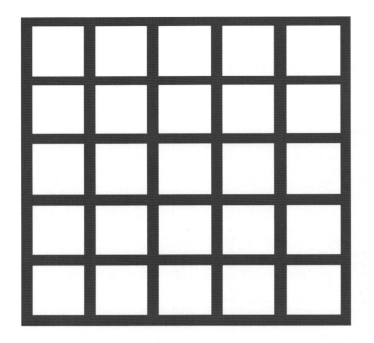

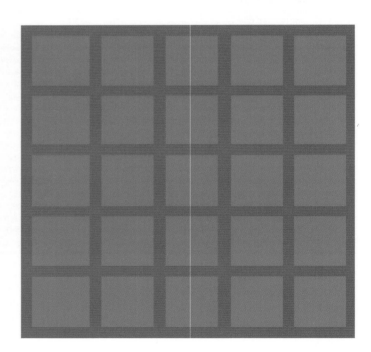

## Isoluminance

Observe the upper blue grid and the alignments of blue squares. Do you perceive 'ghost' gray blobs or smudges at the intersections of the blue and of the white lines? Curiously, the gray blobs disappear when looking directly at an intersection. Now, can you explain why the two lower grids don't have the same optical effect? ('No Martini, no blobs' isn't a good answer!) See page 60

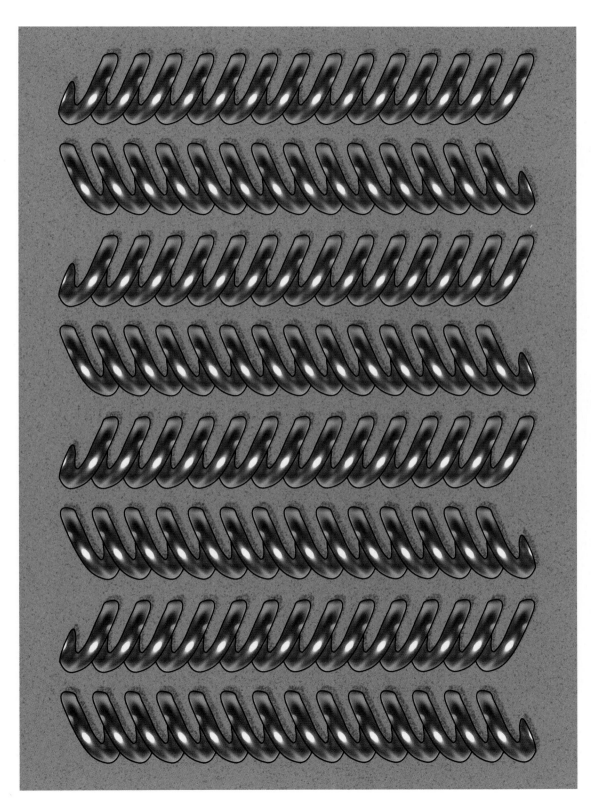

**Aligned springs**
Are the eight spiral springs parallel to each other?
See page 60

## Receding

Relax. Concentrate your gaze on the center of the image. Just concentrate and continue to relax even deeper. Let a peaceful serenity penetrate deeper and deeper to every cell of your mind. Then the spiral pattern of purple discs will shrink slowly – and it isn't your imagination!

See page 60

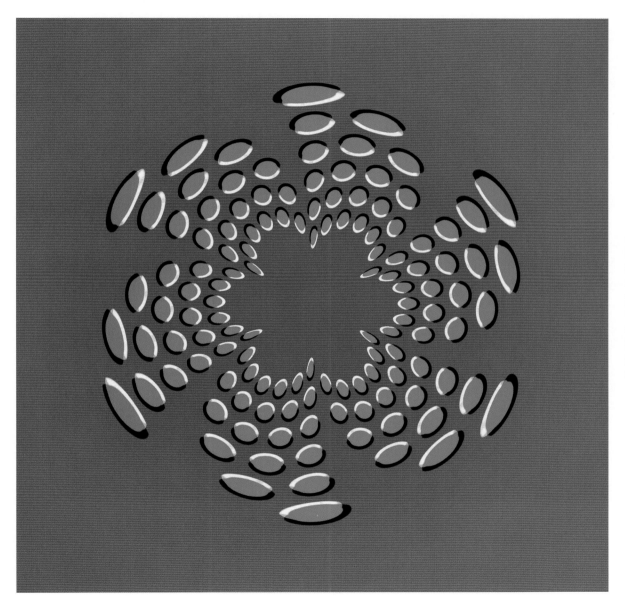

**Advancing**
If you concentrate sufficiently on this drawing, the spiral pattern of green discs seems to expand. The effect is mainly caused by our peripheral vision.

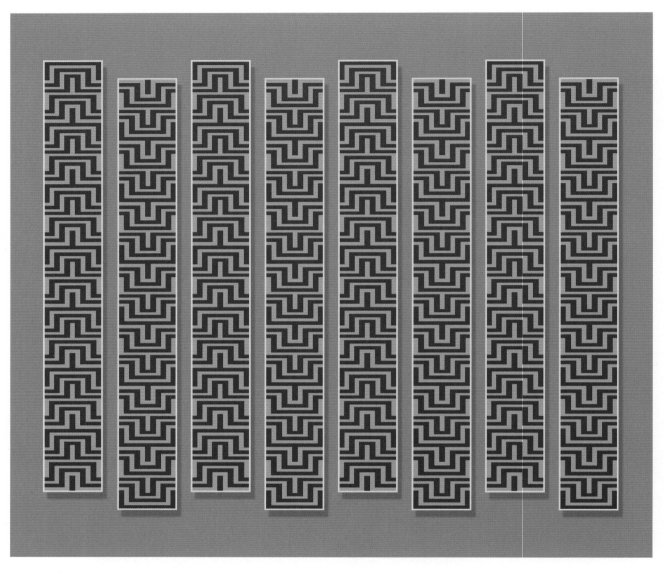

**Aligned slats**
Are the slats perfectly straight and parallel?
See page 60

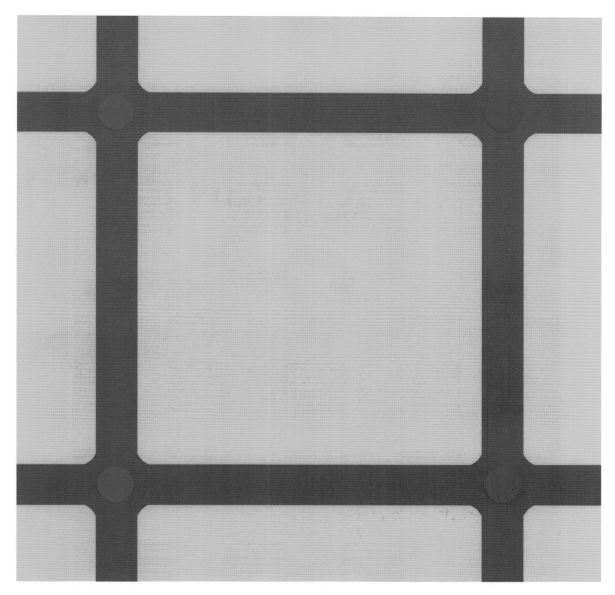

**Flip-flop effect**
Fix your gaze on one of the blue dots and
the blue dots on the opposite intersections
will twinkle!
See page 60

## Color test

Look at the colored pattern from a
distance and guess what color fills the
elongated horizontal blue shapes!
See page 60

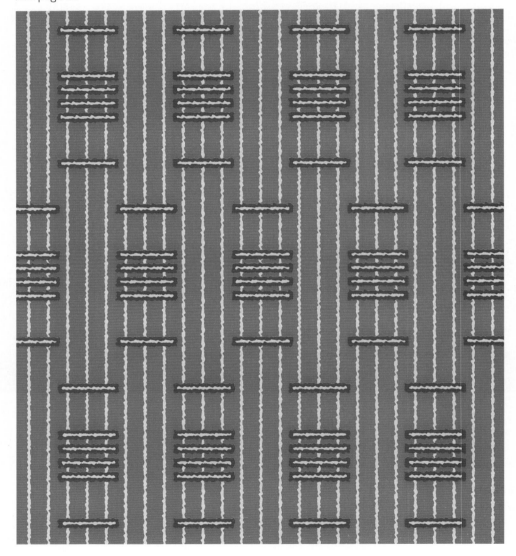

**Cubic boxes**
Both photographs represent two images of the same object taken under different illumination conditions. Now look closely at the square panels of the upper and lower cubic boxes. Which square panels seem darker?
See page 60

**Apparition**
Stare at the small red dot in the middle
of the image for about 30 seconds, then
immediately close your eyes and tilt your
head back. Keep your eyes closed as long
as an aura surrounding a feminine face
appears in your mind. A miracle – or
maybe not? Can you explain this?
See page 61

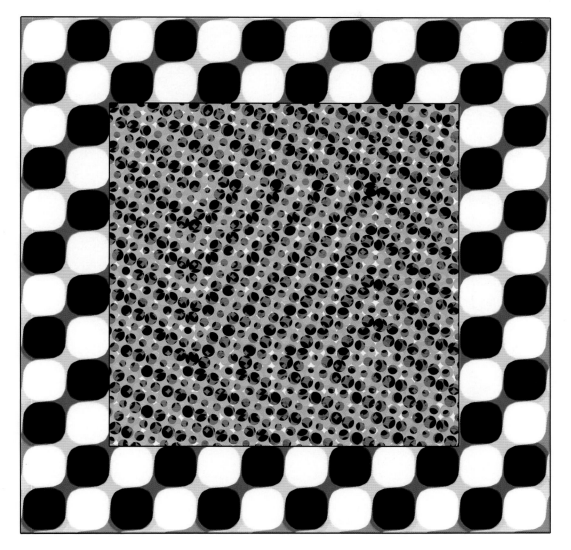

**Tilted square**
Is this square slanted?

See page 61

## Modern wheel

When we observe a two-dimensional picture on paper, we often interpret it as a three-dimensional figure. This insistence on viewing objects as three-dimensional can lead to interesting perceptual problems. For instance, the wheel in the picture is actually an object that cannot exist according to the known laws of physics, even if it has a representation suggesting, at first sight, that it can be constructed! This kind of illusion is known as an impossible or undecidable figure.

**Full moon and eclipse**
Have a look at the two shots representing a full moon and an eclipse. Do you notice something odd about the pictures?
See page 61

**Impossible machine**
Why couldn't this strange mechanical gadget work?
See page 61

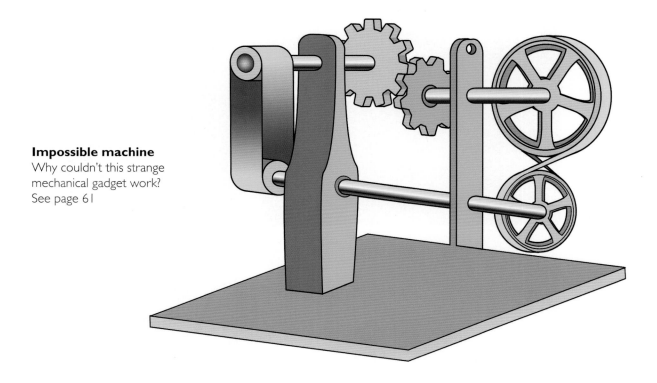

## Length distortion

Despite our ability to estimate size differences in many cases, our ability is distorted by a wide range of factors and even a simple arrangement of lines can be very misleading! For instance, can you say if the red arrow is longer or shorter than the blue one?

See page 61

## Alphabet distortion

Simultaneous orientation contrast occurs even with an arrangement of letters. The columns of Ss and Zs embedded in the blue vertical bars induce a visual distortion; although the blue bars are perfectly straight and parallel, they appear to bulge alternately inward and outward in the middle of the picture. This illusion was created during one of our visual creativity workshops and it resembles the famous 'twisted cord illusion'. The twisted cord illusion is made up of layers of black and white lines all tilted in the same direction. Cells that register the angle of the small individual white and black lines within the cord fire more strongly than cells preferring other degrees of tilt (such as that of the whole cord itself). Curiously, the brain interprets these signals as meaning that the entire cord is tilted. To sum up: for our brain, the whole is always equal to the sum of its parts!

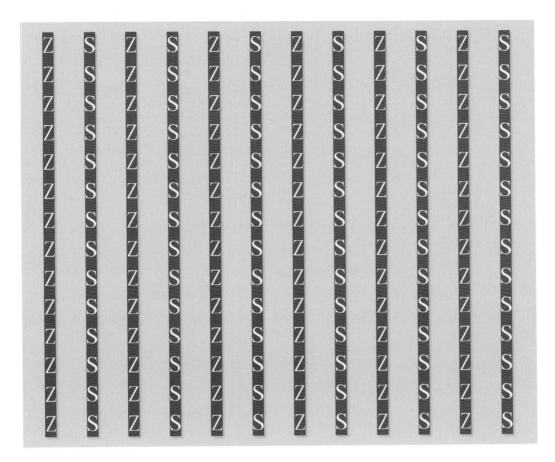

### Alphabet distortion II

Another interesting visual distortion involving alphabet letters, but here the effect is somewhat different. The alternating columns of Ss and Zs embedded in the purple vertical bars induce a tilting sensation. The bars seem to converge or diverge, but they are perfectly straight and parallel.

# Gallery II Solutions

**Vertigo** (page 39)
This is a neat version of the Hering illusion. In fact, this illusion was discovered by the German physiologist Ewald Hering in 1861. The illusion shows two horizontal lines that look as if they are being bent outward when laid over converging radial lines (suggested by the windows of the skyscrapers in our drawing). The distortion is actually produced by the converging lined pattern on the background, which simulates a perspective design and creates a false impression of depth.

**Distorted squares?** (page 41)

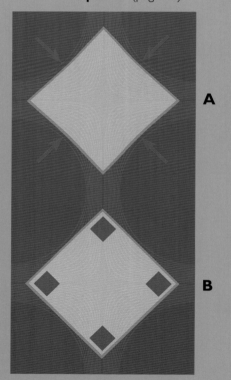

Ninety-nine per cent of people say only square B seems distorted, but the reality is that square A is distorted (concave) while square B isn't. You don't believe it? See the image, or check it with a set-square.
In cases of perceptive distortion, the brain interprets incorrectly (or rectifies wrongly) regular lines or shapes in the foreground in contrast to other regular lines (or shapes) in the background, making them appear distorted. This illusion is related to the Ehrenstein illusion, studied by the German psychologist Walter Ehrenstein, in which the sides of a square lying inside a pattern of concentric circles apparently assume a curved shape.

**Twisted steel ropes** (page 43)
The central set of twisted steel ropes appears to separate from the rest of the picture, giving the ensemble a three-dimensional impression (thanks also to the magnifying glass!) The ropes are perfectly aligned and parallel to each other, though evidence points to the contrary! The 'twisted cord' illusion is probably due to orientation-sensitive simple cells in the striate cortex in our brains, which interact to combine the closely-spaced tilted lines into a single tilted line.

**Isoluminance** (page 44)
There are a lot of explanations and counter-explanations concerning the Herman grid illusion (that's the true name of the illusion). Clearly, scientists don't know exactly what happens here, but what we do know is that when the light contrasts are reduced (isoluminance), the blob optical effect tends to decrease or vanish. Both colors of the yellow grid with the blue insets reflect approximately the same amount of light (in other words, they are equally bright); that's why there aren't any blobs at the intersection of the grid.

**Aligned springs** (page 45)
Even if they seem to diverge slightly, they are perfectly parallel to each other. This is a variant of the classic Zöllner illlusion which traditionally represents a series of parallel lines intersected by transversals, at an angle of 30-40 degrees. These transversals make the parallel lines appear to converge and diverge. The Zöllner illusion may be caused by an impression of depth or be due to a tendency to overestimate acute angles and underestimate obtuse ones.

**Receding** (page 46)
This is another example of the peripheral drift illusion which can be used for hypnotherapy.

**Aligned slats** (page 48)
Yes, they are perfectly straight and parallel. The pattern within the shapes interferes with the orthogonal outlines of the slats. If you observe the picture with half-closed eyes, you may perceive 'subliminal' vertical alignments of arrow-like shapes responsible for the observed optical distortion.

**Flip-flop effect** (page 49)
This is another neat variation of the famous scintillating grid illusion by Lingelbach. The optical effect seems to exist only at intermediate distances; if the eye is moved very close to or very far away from the figure, the effect does not appear.

**Color test** (page 50)
Ninety per cent of people given this test answer 'white', despite the fact that the color inside the horizontal blue rectangles is as yellow as the vertical lines in the background.

**Cubic boxes** (page 51)
In reality, the square panels of the boxes in both photographs are identical and thus have exactly the same brightness! This

optical effect, induced by the contrasting backgrounds, is called simultaneous brightness contrast. Simultaneous contrast can be observed for black and white, as well as for colored images.

## Apparition (page 52)

This phenomenon is known as after-image. An after-image is an optical illusion that occurs after looking away from an image at which you have been gazing fixedly. This is closely related to the phenomenon called the persistence of vision, which is used in animated and live-action movies. After-images are caused when the eye's photo-receptors adapt from the overstimulation and lose sensitivity.

## Tilted square (page 53)

No, it is a perfect right-angled square! Simultaneous orientation contrast is induced by the particular disposition of alternating clear and dark dots within the shape.

## Full moon and eclipse (page 55)

The two moons are physically identical in both shots, even if in the lower image the moon seems darker (actually, the one in the upper image looks like a white disc visible through dark clouds, whereas the moon in the lower image appears as a black disc behind white clouds). The perception of surface lightness is one of the most basic aspects of visual awareness. It is well known that an object with the same brightness can be perceived as darker or lighter according to the context or environment in which it is integrated. The fact that our visual system works 'analogically' and tends to separate the reflected light of a particular surface from the prevailing illumination (or atmospheric conditions) in which it is embedded, generating layered image representations, can play a decisive role in the perception of surface lightness. This lightness optical illusion is based on the work of the cognitive scientists Barton L. Anderson and Jonathan Winawer.

## Impossible machine (page 56)

Because the following items are 'impossible' (from left to right): 1. the belt: 2. the teeth of the gear wheels: 3. the axis of the belt wheels; and, finally, 4. the axle which passes through the two vertical metal pieces. Impossible objects are particular pictures drawn by matching together two or more different points of view of the same object, or by extending and blending together the perspective of one object with that of another one. Some impossible objects are not immediately obvious.

## Length distortion (page 57)

The red arrow is as long as the blue one, but it appears longer than the horizontal arrow because the eye moves more easily from side to side than up and down. The extra effort required to scan a vertical is interpreted by our brain as reflecting a greater distance. This illusion, called the Sarcone-Waeber illusion, also relies on the fact that both discs seem of the same size, whereas the disc which represents the moon (and contains the red arrow) is actually wider due to the Helmholtz irradiation effect. The term 'irradiation' refers to the spreading of light areas into adjacent dark areas, where a shape would get an increase in the size of a bright area at the expense of an adjacent dark area. This creates apparent displacement of a black-white boundary, so that the contour appears shifted in the direction of the dark area.

# Gallery III

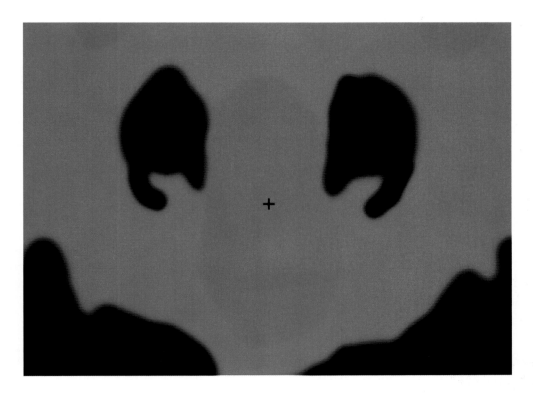

**Tiger tiger**
Stare at the '+' in the middle of the blue picture for about 15 seconds. Then quickly look at the '+' within the picture of a tiger. What happens?
See page 84

**Helicopters**
Which line is longer: red
or blue?
See page 84

**The weight of the convergences**
Which elephant seems heavier?
See page 84

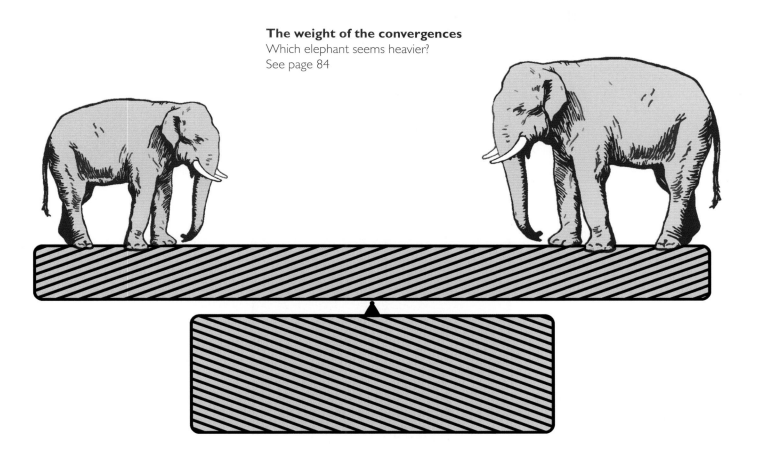

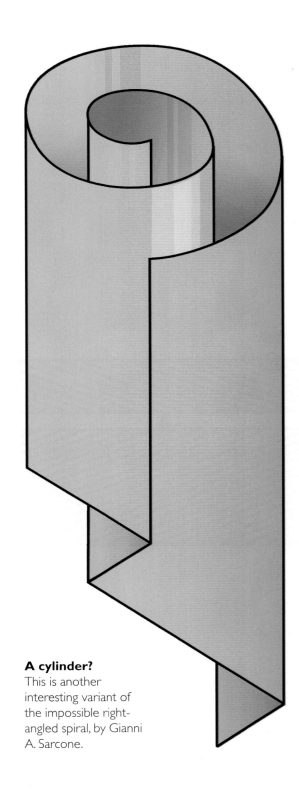

**A cylinder?**
This is another interesting variant of the impossible right-angled spiral, by Gianni A. Sarcone.

## Color assimilation

The foreground concentric yellow discs induce a color change in the
background purple and grey lines. In fact, the segmented purple lines
lying within the discs appear like magenta, while the segmented grey
lines appear more yellowish. This illusion is an example of the color
assimilation or 'spreading' effect that makes colors seem to spread into or
become assimilated into neighboring color areas. Whilst the physiological
mechanisms for color contrast phenomena are well understood, how the
assimilation occurs is not. We know, however, that this effect happens only in
small colored surfaces.

**Klein scissors**

This impossible pair of scissors is useless, but nevertheless interesting. The scissor handles resemble the 'Klein bottle', a one-sided topological surface having no inside or outside.

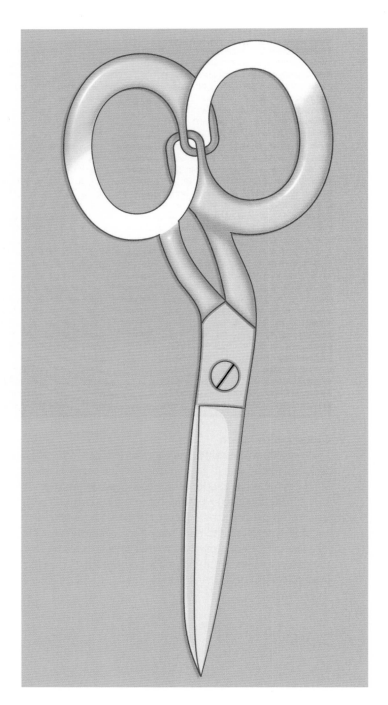

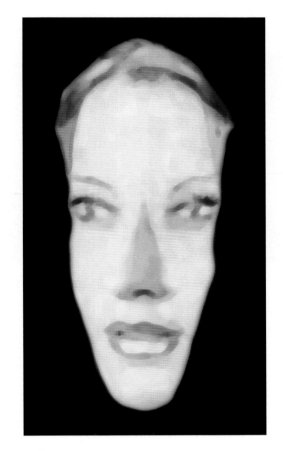

**Follow my nose**
Can you guess where the woman is fixing her gaze: to the left or to the right?
See page 84

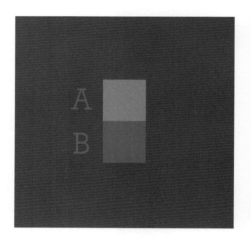 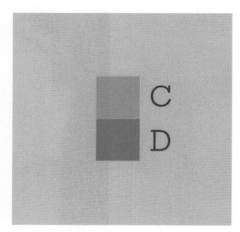

**Blues**

Match the pair of colored squares which have the same hue: A and C, or A and D, or B and C, or maybe B and D?
See page 84

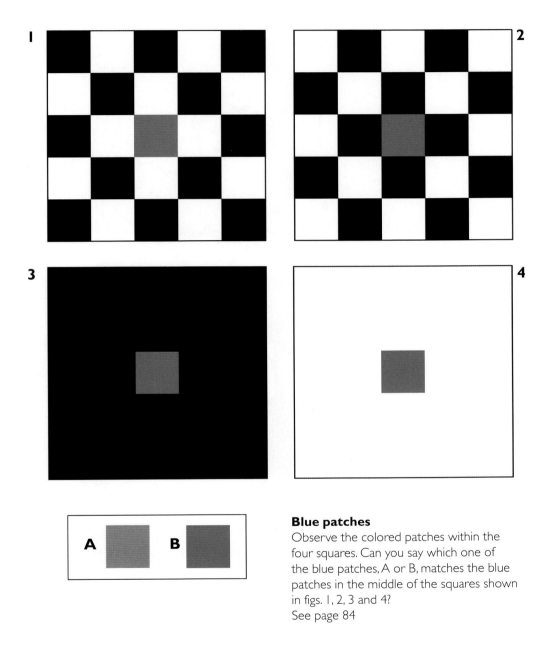

**Blue patches**
Observe the colored patches within the four squares. Can you say which one of the blue patches, A or B, matches the blue patches in the middle of the squares shown in figs. 1, 2, 3 and 4?
See page 84

## Naughty illusion

Yes, our grandfathers too were great teases and appreciated 'subtle' naughty allusions and jokes, such as this drawing which plays on the ambiguity of bald-headed gentlemen who appear also as the large 'chest' of the lady. Postcards with optical illusions such as this were printed in their millions in the early part of the last century.

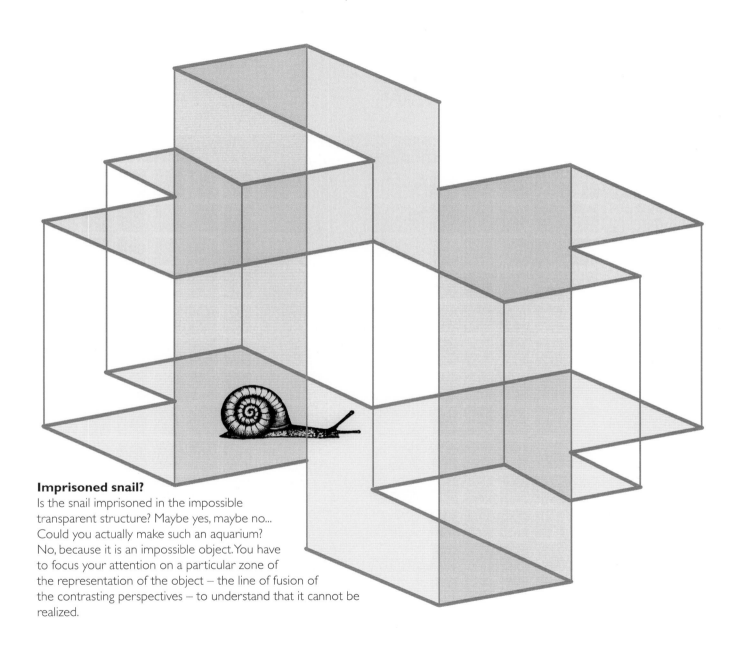

**Imprisoned snail?**

Is the snail imprisoned in the impossible transparent structure? Maybe yes, maybe no... Could you actually make such an aquarium? No, because it is an impossible object. You have to focus your attention on a particular zone of the representation of the object – the line of fusion of the contrasting perspectives – to understand that it cannot be realized.

## Buildings

Do you see some grey dots appearing and vanishing repeatedly at the intersection of the windows? Are the buildings perfectly upright and parallel to each other?
See page 84

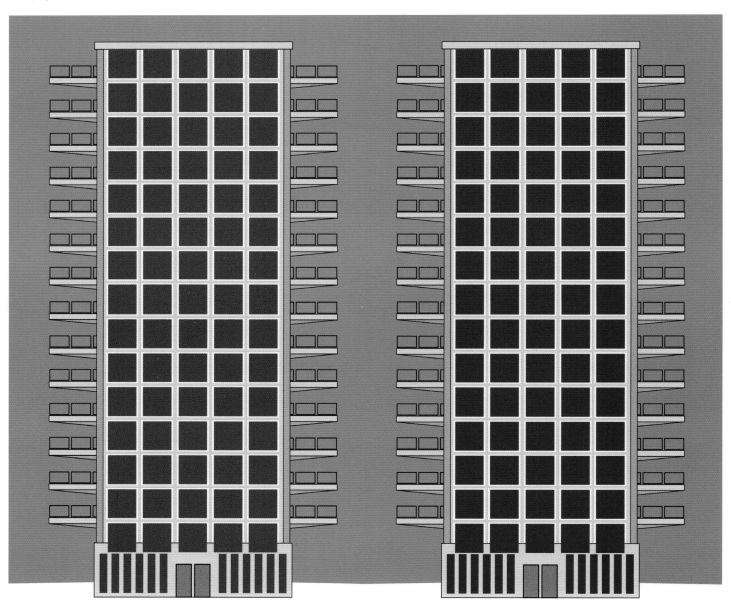

**Patterned bands**
Are the vertical yellow bands parallel to
each other?
See page 84

## Magic disc

If you concentrate on the gradient black zones of the disc, they will appear to expand, but if you concentrate on the grey radial lines that cross the disc, you may perceive a subtle fluid that vibrates and blinks up and down. The blinking effect is due to the lateral inhibition of our visual system.

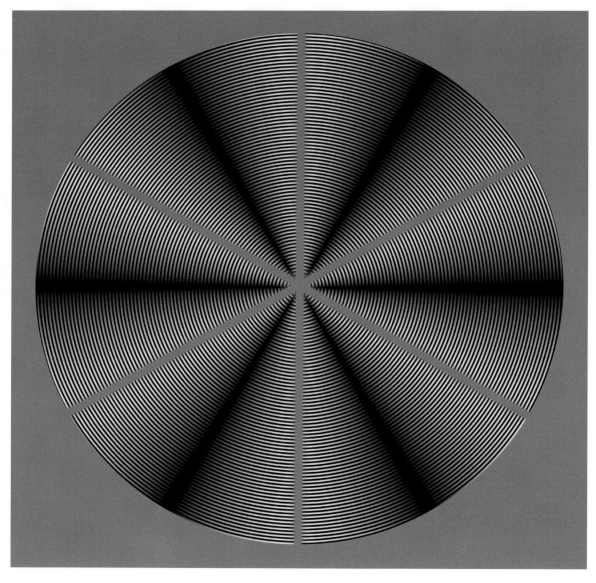

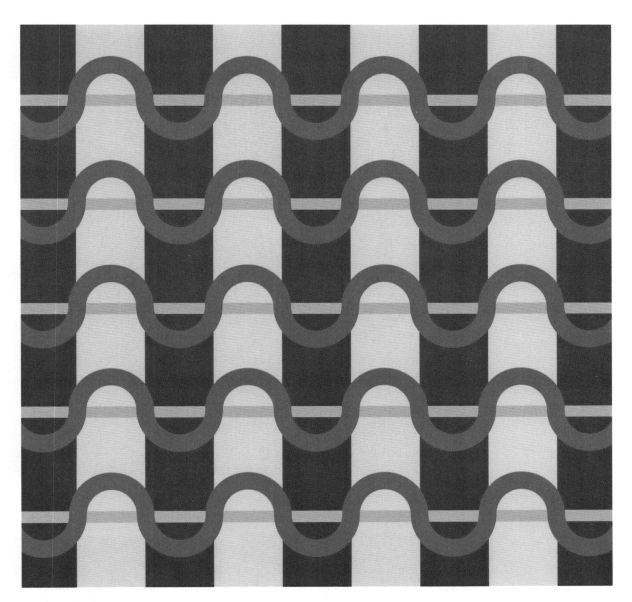

**Grey variations**

The horizontal grey lines running through the alternating black and grey vertical bands are physically homogeneous. The brightness variation of the horizontal lines is due to lateral inhibitory interactions in our visual system. The grey lines seem to be continued through the khaki wavy patterns ('phantom' line segments may be perceived within the wavy patterns near the intersections with the horizontal grey lines).

**A**

**Appearing and disappearing bird**

Reproduce the magic puzzle in A and paste it on to material which is easy to cut (cardboard, foam sheet). Then cut out your puzzle along the dotted lines. The aim of the game is to lay the three puzzle pieces out in order to make an additional bird appear, as shown in B. Easy? Well, try now to explain why a bird reappears or vanishes at will! See page 84

**B**

**Deceiving arcs**
Are the tops of
these cylinder-
like shapes
different (wider
or narrower) than
their respective
bottoms?
See page 84

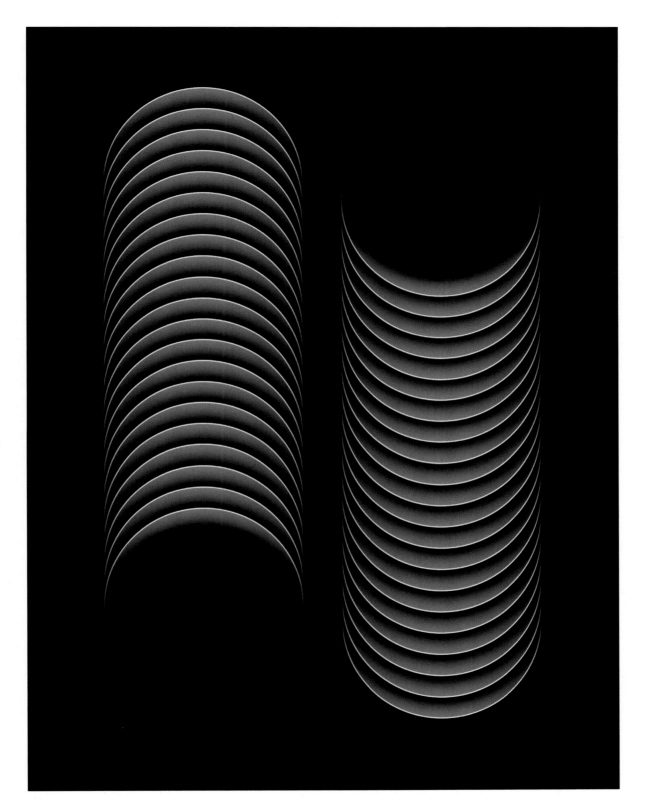

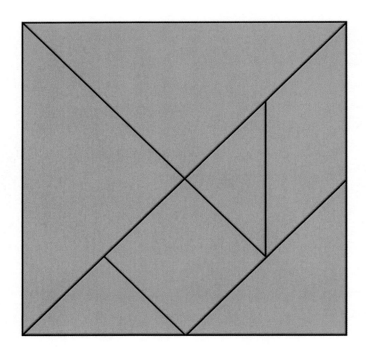

### Tangram alphabet

Here is a visual thinking challenge. Nowadays, the tangram, which is formed from seven polygons, is one of the most popular dissection puzzles. The aim of the puzzle is to rearrange all the geometric pieces to form figures. Reproduce and cut out the tangram puzzle and form, with all its seven pieces, each letter of the alphabet shown in the picture (no overlappings!).
See page 85

### Short history of the tangram

Little is known for certain about the origin of the tangram. Even the origin of the name is obscure! The earliest known book was published around 1813 in China. However, a tangram-like puzzle first appeared in a book published in Japan in 1742. By 1817, tangram publications had appeared in the United States and in Europe.

Scholars assume that tangrams originated from the Orient before the 18th century and then spread westwards. Frankly, in our humble opinion, a lot of 'oriental' games were first created in Europe and then adapted in Asia, such as Chinese checkers, called *tiao qi* in China. In the past, the adjective 'Chinese' was commonly used in the West to denote any odd, complicated or contrived thing and not the origin of the object! Whatever the date at which the tangram was invented, rearrangement puzzles' roots can be traced back to the 3rd century BC. Back in those days Archimedes, a Greek mathematician, designed a tangram-like puzzle called the Loculus Archimedis or Ostomachion.

# Take 1000 and add 40 to it.

## Now add another 1000.

### Now add 30.

### Add another 1000.

### Now add 20.

## Now add another 1000.

### Finally, add 10.

## What is the total?

**Tricky addition: machine versus human**
Ask two friends to follow the simple instructions
on this page. Tell them beforehand that one has to
add up the numbers in his head, while the other
can use a calculator. The final result should be
written down. The first player to find the right total
has won. We'll bet that the calculator always wins!
See page 85

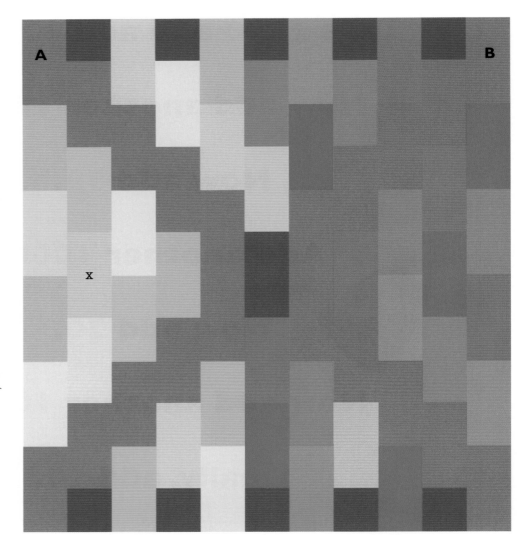

## Seminole color pattern

This interesting color pattern was inspired by a traditional Seminole pattern. Do you notice that the orange stair-like shape B seems slightly brighter than the orange stair-like shape A? Both, however, have the same color hue. This illustrates that the same color affects us differently depending on the adjacent colors. You don't believe it? Try then to guess which color brick has the same color hue as the brick marked with an 'x'!

See page 85

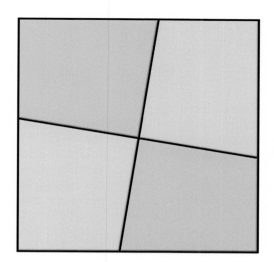

## Square tessellation

A simple slanted quadrilateral repeated at will creates great optic effects and tessellation patterns. To prove the geometry of the tessellation, the quadrilaterals have been alternately painted in white and black. These geometric shapes, called *scutellograms*, have two right angles and two adjacent sides which are equal, and it is sufficient to know the length of just one diagonal to calculate their area.

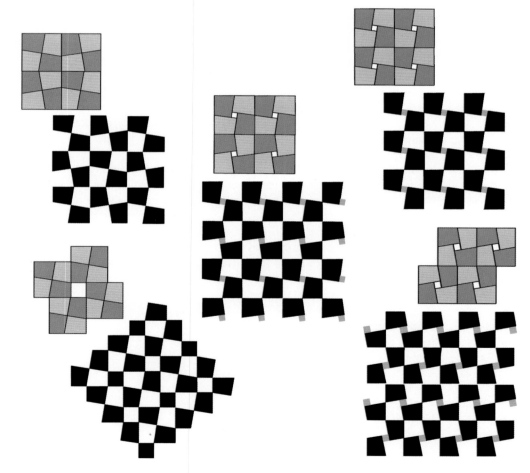

# Gallery III Solutions

**Tiger Tiger** (page 63)
You should see a COLOR image of a tiger. As soon as you move your eyes, however, you'll notice that it immediately becomes black and white! This illusion induces an after-image effect. An after-image is a negative or complementary 'ghost' of a color seen after prolonged stimulation of the eye.

**Helicopters** (page 64)
Strangely, if you concentrate on the ellipses that inscribe the lines, the red line will appear longer. If you concentrate on the helicopters instead, then the blue line will appear longer! Actually, the blue line is really the longest of both lines.

**The weight of the convergences** (page 65)
Neither! The balance is perfectly level, even though it seems to tilt to the right. The visual distortion is induced by the contrast between the inset patterns of tilted lines and the outlines of the rectangles which represent the balance.

**Follow my nose** (page 69)
If you focus your attention on her nose, you will notice after a while that it is an 'undecidable figure'. The nose (and thus the face) changes orientation depending on your point of view or your hand preference. About 90 per cent of right-handed persons shown this image consider the nose points to the left, while about 60 per cent of left-handed persons think it points to the right! Impossible figures aren't created to baffle your eyes; their structure should appear coherent and logical. They are designed to confuse your MIND.

**Blues** (page 70)
The blue square A has exactly the same hue as the blue square D, despite the simultaneous color contrast effect which makes the square A appear brighter than the square D.

**Blue patches** (page 71)
The blue patch B corresponds to ALL the blue patches in figs. 1, 2, 3 and 4, even though the blue patches in figs. 1 and 3 appear slightly brighter compared to those in figs. 2 and 4. Interestingly, despite being immediately surrounded by white squares, the blue patch in fig. 1 appears brighter than the same patch in fig. 2, surrounded by black squares. This is apparently at odds with a 'simultaneous color contrast' explanation! This optical illusion is based on Devalois' checkerboard illusion.

**Buildings** (page 74)
The apparition of grey dots is induced by lateral inhibition of our visual system. Yes, the buildings are perfectly vertical and parallel to each other.

**Patterned bands** (page 75)
Yes, it seems incredible, but they are perfectly parallel to each other! This illusion is related to the well-known Café Wall and Twisted Cord illusions.

**Appearing and disappearing bird** (page 78)
Vanish puzzles are a kind of geometric 'paradox' that involves the cutting and rearranging of a drawing. Actually, the bird in the picture reappears or disappears because of the redistribution of single image portions. The principle is as if we had nine full glasses of water and put a little bit of each one into an empty tentth glass. At the end of it all, it will APPEAR that we magically filled 10 glasses with only nine full glasses! In short, the more birds there are, the thinner they are... One of the most famous vanish puzzles was Sam Loyd's Get Off the Earth puzzle made in 1896. Another early example is The Vanishing Leprechaun. The first example of a vanishing area puzzle, however, was reported in the book *Libro d'Architettura Primo* by Sebastiano Serlio, an Italian architect of the Renaissance (even though Serlio didn't notice any area had actually vanished!). The first description and mathematical explanation of the vanish paradox was found in a maths puzzle book with a very long title: *Rational Recreations in Which the Principles of Numbers and Natural Philosophy Are Clearly and Copiously Elucidated, by a Series of Easy, Entertaining, Interesting Experiments Among Which Are All Those Commonly Performed With the Cards* by William Hooper (1774).

**Deceiving arcs** (page 79)
The repetition of a simple geometric form can produce a three-dimensional effect and induce shape distortions. The two cylinder-like shapes consist simply of a series of arcs having all exactly the same size; thus, the sides of both shapes should appear to be parallel, but to most people the bottoms of the shapes are perceived as wider than the tops.

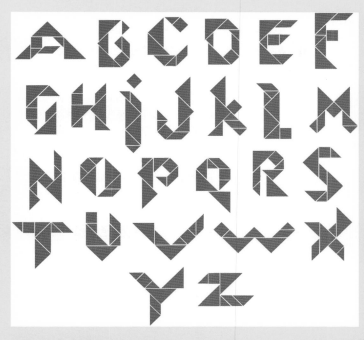

**Tangram alphabet** (page 80)

**Tricky addition: machine versus human** (page 81)
The calculator wins because your friend who made the addition in his head is certain to write the number 5,000 down, instead of 4,100, the correct answer. This kind of cognitive error occurs very frequently when we calculate with tens and thousands.

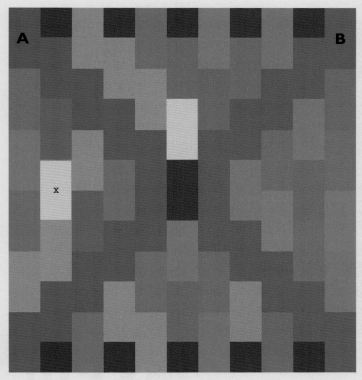

**Seminole color pattern** (page 82)
Here are the two bricks of the same color hue. We bet you didn't find them!

# Gallery IV

## Double-pan precision balance

Some things appear impossible until you understand them and then they become trivial or, as Jean-Luc Picard in *Star Trek* used to say, 'Things are only impossible until they're not.' It's just a question of mental VISION! Well, using just pure logic, try to solve the following puzzle, which on the face of it seems impossible to solve. Weighing from 1 to 60 grams using test weights on one side of a balance is possible with weights (calibration masses) of 1, 2, 4, 8, 16 and 32 grams. But is this possible with another sextuplet of weights or, better still, by using a lesser number of test weights (for example, four test weights instead of six)?

See page 108

A 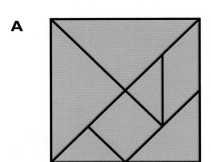   B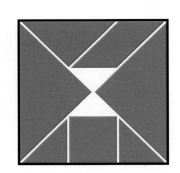

## Tangram paradox

Take the tangram puzzle
you have just realized in the
previous pages and form the
squares shown in A. and B.
Strangely, both the 'squares' are
made from the same seven
tangram pieces. Then why are
two small triangles missing in
the second one? Now form,
using these seven pieces, the
yellow figures shown in the
black tables. Finally, form their
black counterparts in the
yellow tables. In both cases, you
have to use all seven pieces!
Try to explain why a small
triangular element is missing in
the black figures.

See page 108

## Expanding rosace

Fix your gaze at the center of the rosace until the color disc expands. This is a geometric peripheral drift illusion.

## The happy/unhappy girl

Yes, the girl seems very angry, but seen at a certain distance (from two metres) she will begin to smile and show a more charming facial expression. This illusion is a kind of ambiguous bistable figure and is produced by merging two pixel matrixes having different resolutions. When you see the image more closely, the 'fine' pixels will dominate (unhappy girl), but when you observe the image from a distance, the 'large' pixels become apparent (happy girl). This illusion is based on Salvador Dalí's optic artwork 'Gala Contemplating the Mediterranean Sea Which at Twenty Meters Becomes the Portrait of Abraham Lincoln,' 1976.

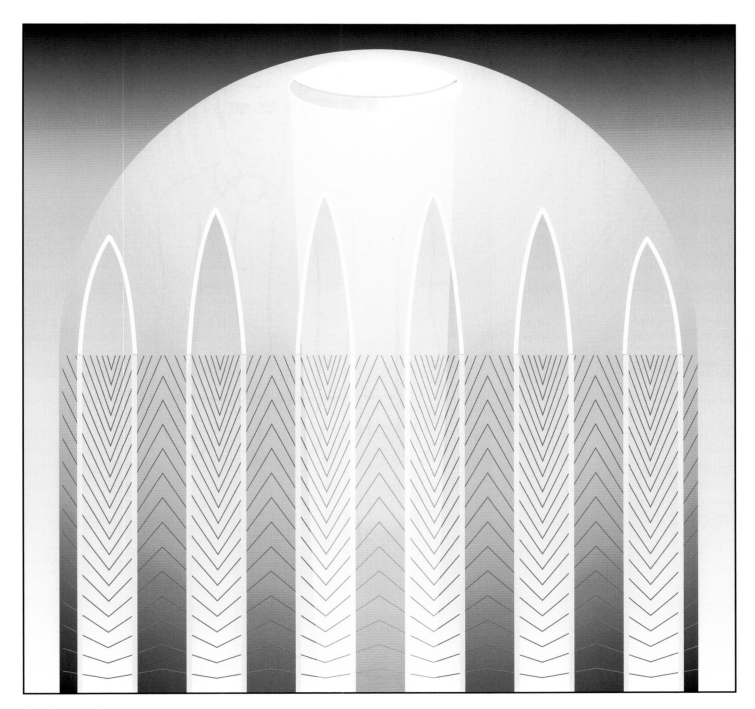

**Mystic temple**
Do the white vertical lines
tend to bend in at the top?
See page 108

**Two men in one**

Ever wonder what a woman's dream is really about? Women dream of exotic, impossible things!

## Textile pattern illusions

Some textile patterns can induce curious visual distortions. In
1860 the German astrophysicist Johann Karl Zöllner was the first
to notice the optical illusion in a pattern designed for a print for
dress fabric. This classic illusion was subsequently named after its
discoverer. Herringbone weaves, a type of twill weave in which the
chevron pattern alternates direction, creating a zigzag effect, are
very similar to the Zöllner illusion. Houndstooth checks, patterns
made up of squares with drawn-out corners that link them
together, can also produce an interesting tilting effect, as illustrated
in the drawing!

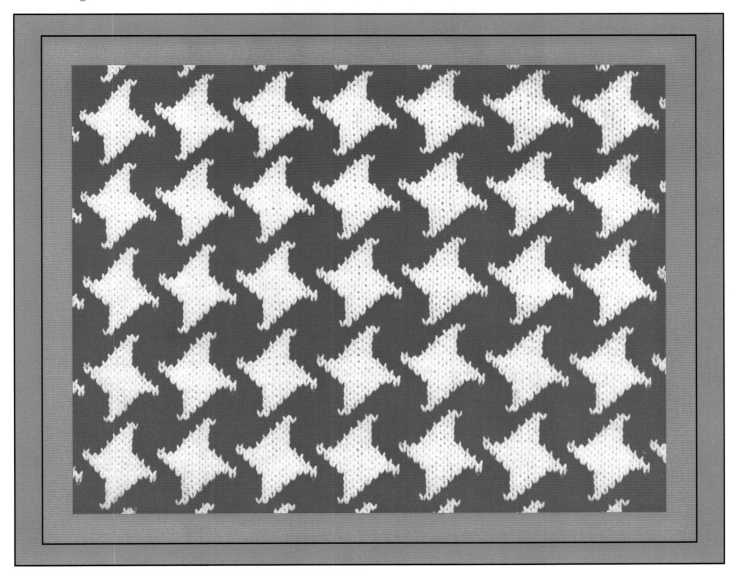

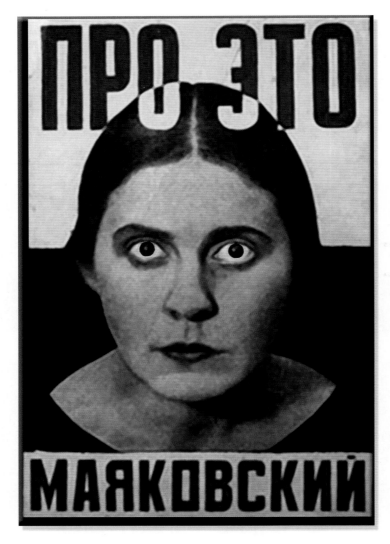

**Magnetic eyes**
This notable illustration by Aleksandr Rodchenko (1923) was used for the cover of a book of poems by Vladimir Mayakovsky. From whichever point you look at the woman, she seems to be gazing at you!

**Haze and flowers**
Do you notice something particular in this
poetic scene?
See page 108

**Gas flames**

This photo shows the blue flames from a gas stove in the dark. The flames seem to move slightly and to expand, especially when you move closer and further from the image. This is a kind of peripheral drift illusion.

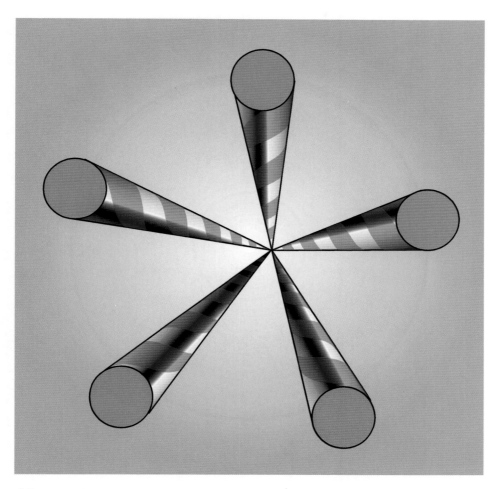

**Alignments**

The five cylinders seem to meet at a single vanishing point in space. Can you find in the drawing two segments which are perfectly co-linear (lying in the same straight line or linear sequence)?

See page 108

## Moving wheels

Move your eyes around the page and the wheels will appear to rotate slightly. This peripheral drift illusion is perfect for web pages or desktop wallpapers!

**Colonial souvenirs**
Did the man wearing the colonial-style
pith helmet in this vintage 1910 photo
really shake the hand of the man with the
bow tie?
See page 109

**Twins**
Are the sisters the same size?
See page 109

## Historical faces

How many people can you spot in the picture? This intriguing picture was created by Norman Parker, a retired biology teacher who has made surrealist paintings for 50 years. We especially like the way Norman camouflages and incorporates objects in his pictures. See page 109

## Mona Lisa

Observe the picture of the Mona Lisa from a distance. Do you notice something particular in the picture? This version of La Gioconda by Leonardo da Vinci was created by Craig S. Kaplan, an assistant professor of computer science at the University of Waterloo in Ontario, Canada. He studies the interactions between computer graphics, art and mathematics. See page 109

## Christmas lights
The colored curved 'neons' seem to
vibrate and blink forward and backward!

## Coaxial axis?

Do the green rings have a common axis? In fact, the inner ring appears to be off-centre. Moreover, the rings seem to counter-rotate when we approach or move away from the picture while fixating on its centre.

See page 109

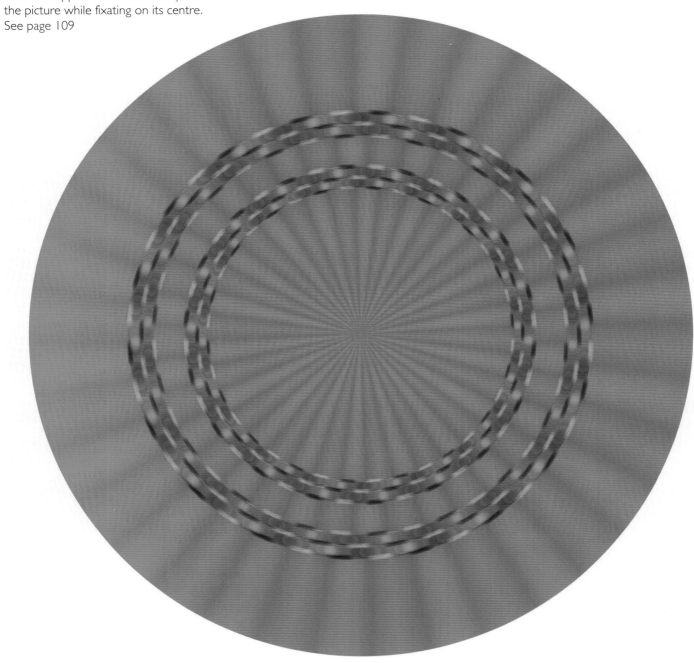

**Gray patches**
Are the gray patches forming a diamond-like shape in the first image as bright as the gray patches of the diamond-like shape in the second image?
See page 109

## Dilating baseball home plates

The spiralling arrangement of baseball home plates
seems to dilate and expand. This illusion works
better within your peripheral vision field.

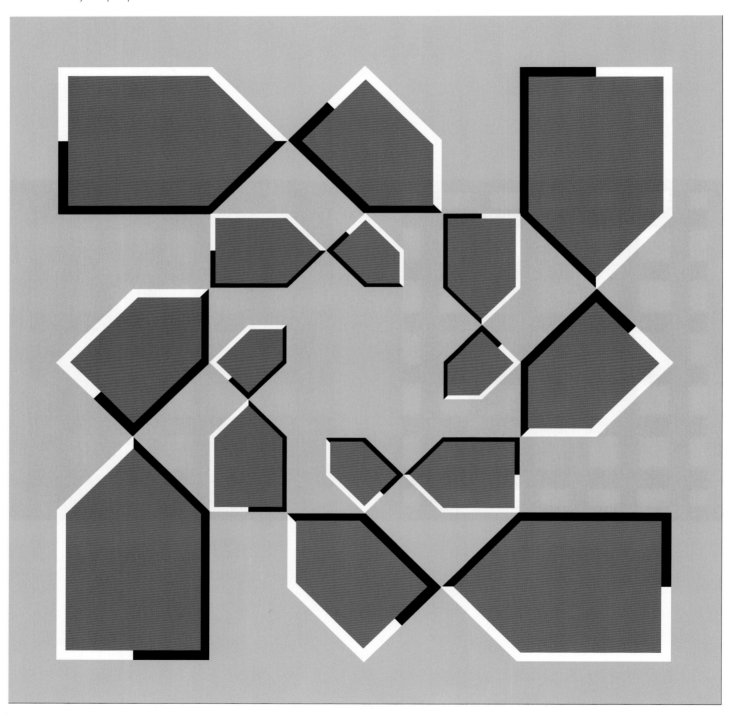

## Twisted squares

The disposition of the geometric shapes makes the inner square tilt in contrast to the yellow square frame.

# Gallery IV Solutions

**Double-pan precision balance** (page 87)
If both sides of the balance can be used, then five test weights from the powers of three will suffice (1, 3, 9, 27, 81) to measure all the weights up to 121 grams:
1, 3-1, 3, 3+1, 9-(3+1), 9-3, (9+1)-3, 9-1, 9, 9+1, (9+3)-1, 9+3, 9+3+1, 27-(9+3+1), etc. However, for measuring weights up to 60 grams there are also many other alternative solutions:
1, 3, 9, 20, 27, or even 1, 2, 7, 19, 31... etc.
Why isn't it possible to determine weights from one to 60 using only four weights (calibration masses)? Because:
A) If test weights are on one side only, then each weight can have one of two states: 1) 'on the scale' or 2) 'off'.
With only five weights, only 32 cases can be achieved (including 'all off' = 0). Therefore, six test weights at least are required for measuring weights up to 60 grams.
B) If test weights are on both sides, each weight can have one of three states: 1) 'on left side', 2) 'on right side', or 3) 'off'.
With only four test weights, 34 or 81 states can be achieved. One is 'all off' = 0. The other 80 comprise 40 pairs where the positions of the weights are mirrored. Thus, four test weights can give only 40 unique overall weights...
But there is a LOGICAL way to determine weights from one to 60 using only four test weights! When considering weights from one to 60 grams, to measure 60 discrete weights, you need only to verify 30 discreet weights. From one to 100 grams, you would need 50, not 100 etc. The logic is as follows:
- NOT 0, NOT 2, then 1
- NOT 2, NOT 4, then 3
- NOT 4, NOT 6, then 5... etc.
As you can see, you need only even test weights! Then, for measuring one to 60

grams four weights (calibration masses) are sufficient. If both sides of the balance can be used, you can use the test weights 2g, 6g, 18g and 54g as follows:
2, 6-2, 6, 6+2, 18-(6+2), 18-6, (18+2)-6, 18-2, 18, 18+2, (18+6)-2, 18+6, 18+6+2, 54-(18+6+2), 54-(18+6)... 54+6.

**Tangram paradox** (page 88)
The black figures appear to be the same – minus a triangular element – as the yellow ones. This seems true only at first glance; in reality, they are a little bit LARGER (measure them)! So nothing disappeared; the missing triangles are just redistributed differently in the whole surface and they are compensated for by a larger figure.

**Mystic temple** (page 91)
No, the lines are perfectly straight and parallel. It's just another interesting illusion involving simultaneous orientation contrast.

**Haze and flowers** (page 95)
Interestingly, this Japanese drawing is made up with only white vertical stripes! The depth sensation and the shadows are created just by adapting the width of the white stripes.

**Alignments** (page 97)
The segments which outline the cylinders appear to be convex to each other, but there are at least two segments which are perfectly co-linear:

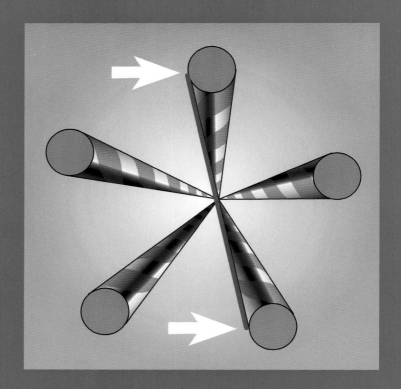

**Colonial souvenirs** (page 99)
No. Do you really think that a man wearing a pith helmet consents to have another man's hand lying on his thigh? The illusion effect of the photo was purely accidental.

**Twins** (page 100)
Yes, both sisters are exactly the same size. Actually, there are no differences except the fact that one is digitally copied and placed further away than the other. This illusion is mainly caused by the strong perspective impression of the corridor. The perceived or relative size of objects depends primarily on the visual angle subtended by the object on the retina in our eyes. The visual angle is dependent on the real size of the object and on the distance the object is from our eyes. When we see two objects with the same relative size, the object which seems more distant is always perceived as being larger. This illusion is related to the Ponzo illusion.

**Historical faces** (page 101)
There are three Winston Churchill faces hidden in the outlines of the leaves. This is a mighty figure/ground illusion!

**Mona Lisa** (page 102)
The picture of the Mona Lisa, from TSP Art, is represented completely by a single non-intersecting path that wiggles and bends to cover the canvas. The path is derived automatically by a computer. The computer covers the original image with points, and then tries to connect the points into a path by solving the Travelling Salesman Problem, a famous (and famously difficult) problem in computer science. The computer's solutions are far from perfect, but more than good enough to produce attractive images! The red filling-in of the picture outline (see the picture above right) reveals that it is a kind of *Jordan's curve*, a curve that is closed and does not intersect itself.

**Coaxial axis?** (page 104)
The rings are perfectly circular and coaxial to each other. This is a circular Zöllner illusion. The contrasting angular direction of the patterns within the circular insets is responsible for the illusion.

**Gray patches** (page 105)
Yes, they have exactly the same hue and brightness, even though the gray patches of the diamond-like shape in the first image appear darker. This is a simultaneous brightness contrast illusion.

# Gallery V

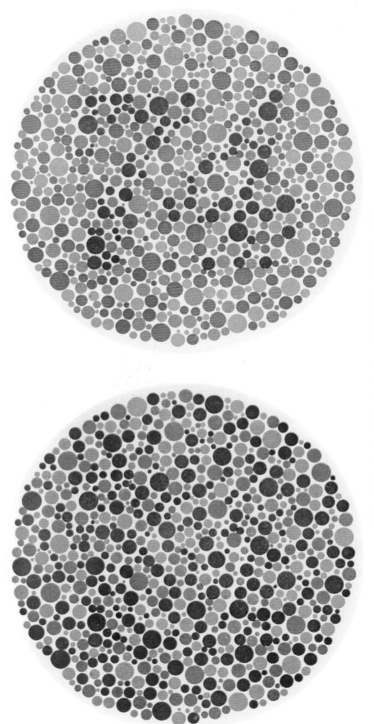

## Ishihara color test

Color deficiency is a condition in which certain colors cannot be distinguished. It is usually an inherited condition. The most commonly used test to detect color deficiencies was developed by the Japanese ophthalmologist Shinobu Ishihara (1879–1963). While working at the Military Medical School he was asked to devise a test to screen military recruits for abnormalities of color vision. His assistant was a colorblind physician who helped him test the plates. Observe the upper color plate. What number do you see revealed in the patterns of dots? The lower plate shows how a man or woman affected with color deficiency may see the upper color plate. This test is designed to give a quick assessment of color vision, and should not replace evaluation by a professional!

See page 132

**A web-footed bird?**
What kind of bird does this silhouette
represent?
See page 132

**The impossible square**
Reproduce and cut out the quadrilaterals
and fit all the nine pieces of the puzzle
together to form a square (there are three
possible solutions!).
See page 132

## Boxed boxes

With three straight cuts, dissect the boxes and reassemble their pieces to make a larger one. See page 132

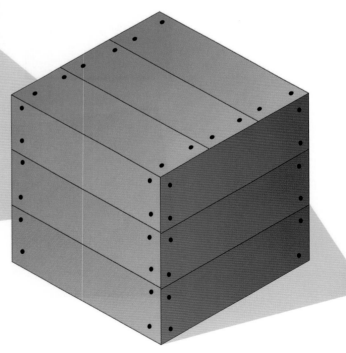

**Dalí's vision**
The surrealist painter Salvador Dalí made this photomontage (1932) starting from a winter sports postcard depicting skiers in a slalom event. With a few pen strokes around the skiers he succeeded in making a double-meaning image: puppies/skiers. Instead of mailing boring postcards to your friends, try to modify them with just a pinch of fantasy first!

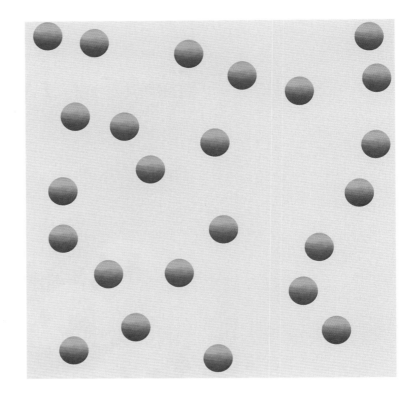

## Gradient camouflage

Observe how the same arrangement of dots filled with a gradient hue seems different when lying on sand ripples. Some dots become more apparent, while others become quite invisible, though all the dots in the picture have exactly the same gradient and the same hue. 'Gradient-gradient illusions' are very common in nature. Most animals display a gradient camouflage to blend in with the surrounding environment. Gradient colors instead of solid colors in disruptive camouflage patterns would enhance greatly the camouflage effectiveness of military uniforms! Interesting to know: the first mass-produced military camouflage material was the Italian *telo mimetico* ('mimetic cloth') pattern of 1929, used to cover a half-shelter.

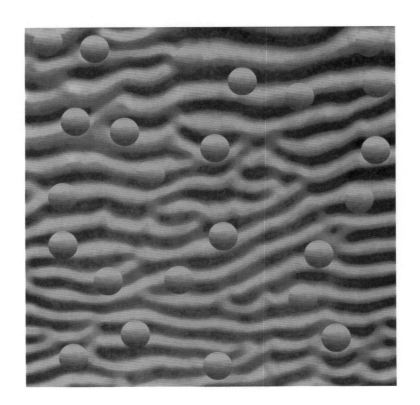

**Ghost biker**

This photo was taken by the French photographer Hughes Leglise Bataille under the 'Grande Arche de La Défense' in Paris, through the colored glass permanent installation. You can see more intriguing photos in his online personal gallery (flickr. com/photos/hughes_leglise). Leglise is a master of light and observation. Light is putty in his competent hands.

## Undisciplined match

A performer takes an ordinary box of matches, opens it at the end and shows it to you (the heads of the matches are all at the other end of the box). Then, closing the box in front of you, he gives it a shake and reopens it. Now you can see one match inside the box turned round (fig. B)! How can such a magic trick can be performed?

See page 132

A

B

**TangraMagic**

Reproduce and cut out the 10-piece puzzle along the dotted lines. Then put the pieces together in order to make the Japanese calligraphy 'sekishu no koe' appear (fig. A). 'Sekishu no koe' (what is the sound of one hand clapping?) refers to the clapping sound that one hand would make: that is to say, the sound of silence.

See page 133

**A**

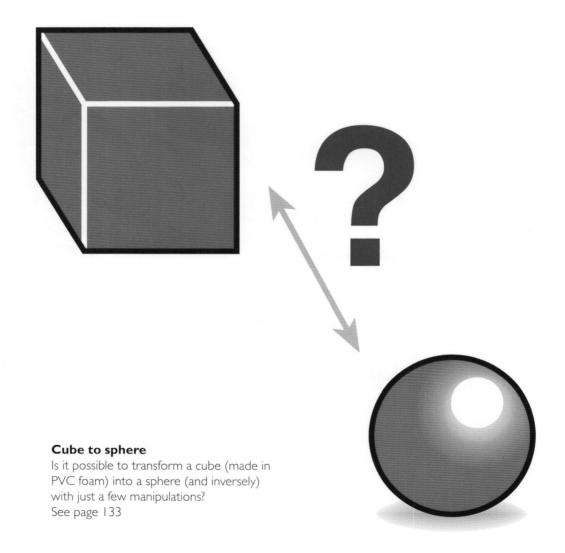

**Cube to sphere**
Is it possible to transform a cube (made in
PVC foam) into a sphere (and inversely)
with just a few manipulations?
See page 133

**Warship**

Have a look at this old photo. Can you say
how many warships are in this fleet?
See page 133

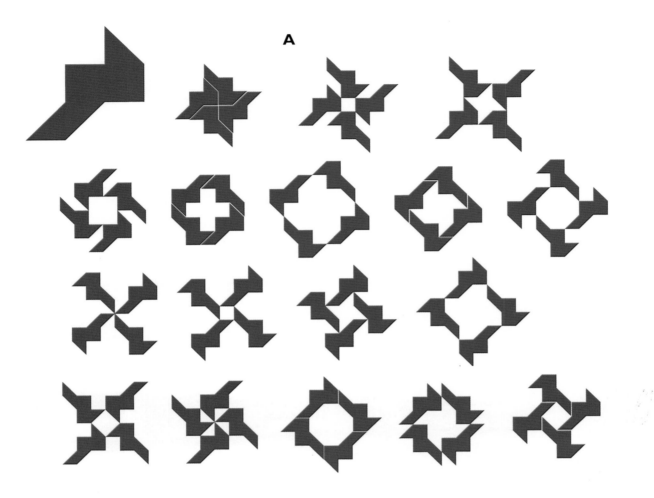

**A**

## View the rainbow in profile

Knowing the essential meaning of the images that surround us enlarges our vision of reality and allows us to create a new reality. Opening one's eyes wider in the creative process is essential in realizing innovative ideas. For example, everybody remembers the pyramid-shaped milk cartons, but not so many know that these cartons were made from an initial cylinder shape (by closing the top and the base of a cylinder shape in a certain manner, as depicted in the image, right). This affects the manufacturing process, saving time and material. Inventiveness is a result of looking for an elegant short-cut to reach a visual or technical effect. The picture

above shows an example of Bruno Munari's exercise designed to stimulate visual creativity. Moving four identical basic pieces through a point of symmetry makes kaleidoscopic patterns appear. It's a purely aesthetic exercise. Can you find new patterns? A company in Genoa called Artegioco adopted Bruno Munari's method for its visual creativity workshops. Coca Frigerio has been Bruno Munari's collaborator for a long time and, along with his associate Alberto Cerchi, offers educational workshops based on signs, textures, volumes and colors. If you'd like to know more about their activities, visit their site (www.giocareconlarte.com).

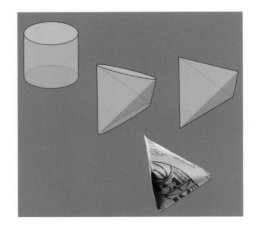

## Sylvester the cat

The cat in the picture is our best assistant. His name is Sylvester and he often frequents our studio because he has adopted a comfortable chair as his second bed. Stare for a while at the eyes of our sleeping assistant. Don't you then have the impression that his eyes seem open? The strange stripe pattern around his closed eyes (fig. A) reproduces roughly the outlines of real cat eyes (fig. B). Animals convey signals through the eyes, so these 'subjective eyes' could be useful to scare off eventual predators during his sleep, but also, when he is awake, make his eyes larger than they really are, like natural eyeliner. This kind of visual mimicry is similar to the 'eye-spots' of some butterflies.

**A**

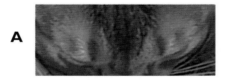

**B**

## Sculptures

Can you find what these three modern
sculptures have in common?

See page 133

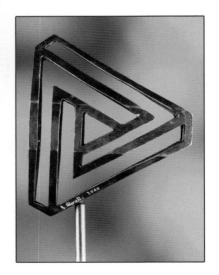

**Psycho-Mona**

The concentric sets of color dots create this psychedelic Mona Lisa. The picture is best viewed from a distance. Do you notice the blue neon radial lines that converge to the center of the picture? They are partial optical illusions… In fact, some small white zones appear blue due to color assimilation.

**Bulging frames**
Are the color frames perfect squares?
See page 133

## Chinese table

Carlo Suares once expressed a great thought: 'A table has four legs. A table with a broken leg remains a table. But a table from which the four legs have been removed becomes only a flat piece of wood. At what moment did it cease to be a table?' However, a table like this one has ceased to be a table even with four legs! Maybe you don't believe us? Why don't you try to make it out of cardboard?

**The face of Paris**
Look at the picture for a while… And then the real face of Paris will suddenly appear!

**The fifth pig**
This is a propaganda visual puzzle from World War Two. Reproduce the puzzle and follow the folding instructions to find the fifth pig.

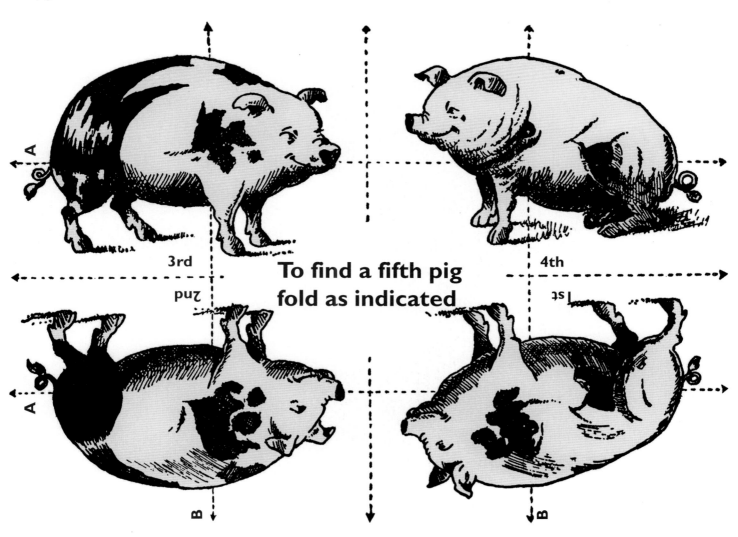

To find a fifth pig
fold as indicated

## Hidden animal
Which animal is hidden in the picture?
See page 133

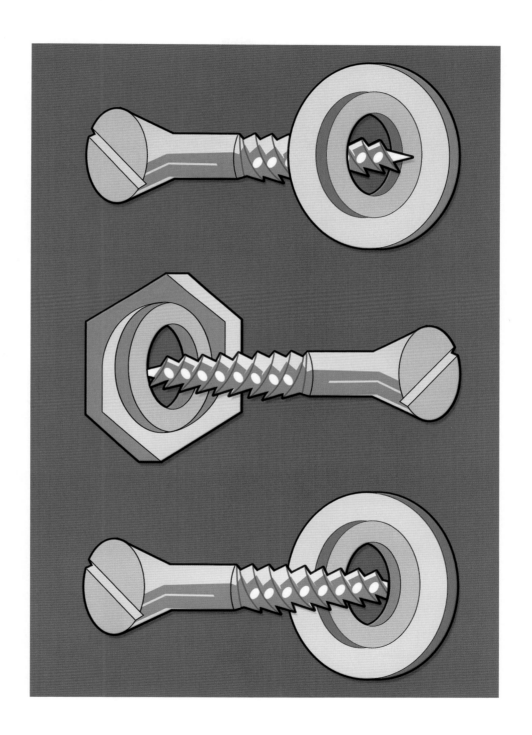

**A screwy vision**
Improbable screws and washers…

# Gallery V Solutions

**Ishihara color test** (page 111)

If you can read the number 74 you're OK, but if you read 21 instead you are probably affected by color deficiency. About eight per cent of men (and fewer women) have some form of color deficiency. Red/green color deficiency is by far the most common form (about 99 per cent) and causes problems in distinguishing these two colours. Another color deficiency, blue/yellow, also exists but is rare and there is no commonly available test for it. Some cases of acquired color vision loss may appear in only one eye and last for only a short time. Most color vision-deficient individuals compensate well for their abnormality and usually rely on color cues and details that are not consciously evident to persons with typical color vision.

**A web-footed bird?** (page 112)

The image blends a flying goose silhouette (B) with a hawk silhouette (C) and can be interpreted differently according to the flight direction. The ratio of head to tail (A) is important to recognize a bird of prey from a web-footed bird; chickens know it instinctively! When chickens are tested with a cardboard reproduction of the silhouette moving overhead, there is no effect – until the silhouette is reversed to

look like a hawk, triggering a characteristic escape response; the chickens will then crouch or run. Hawk silhouettes are also frequently used to help reduce bird collisions with windows or doors. Placing a hawk silhouette on your window or door discourages birds from flying in this direction, because most smaller birds fear and avoid the company of hawks.

**The impossible square** (page 113)

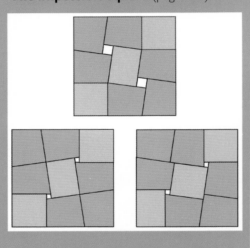

**Boxed boxes** (page 114)

With three straight cuts, dissect the small box and rearrange its pieces around the large box as shown in the example.

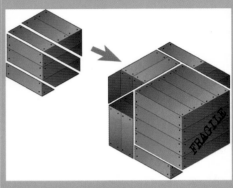

**Undisciplined match** (page 118)

This trick can be performed by hiding the match inside the box as shown in the illustration, so that the match is placed over the edge of the tray of the box. While closing the box, you press this extra match with your thumb and it falls down into place!

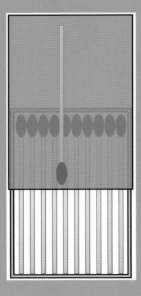

**TangraMagic** (page 119)
To finish the puzzle, one piece must
be left.

**Cube to sphere** (page 120)
Yes, it is possible to transform a foam cube
into a sphere if the cube has a hidden
spherical cavity!

**Bulging frames** (page 126)
The frames seem to bulge inward because
the circular lines distort our perception.
The frames are, however, perfect squares.
This is a variant of the Ehrenstein illusion, in
which the sides of a square placed within
a pattern of concentric circles apparently
take on a curved shape.

**Hidden animal** (page 130)
A swimming dolphin (picture courtesy of
www.coolbubble.com).

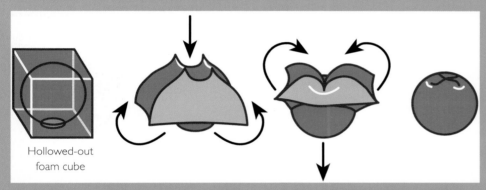

Hollowed-out
foam cube

**Warship** (page 121)
Only one, cleverly camouflaged.

**Sculptures** (page 124)
The three pictures show the same
sculpture from three different views! This
sculpture was created by Guido Moretti,
the master of ambiguous illusion sculptures.
Most of Moretti's sculptures, when seen
from their frontal view, make a classic
optical illusion clearly visible (here, Necker's
cube), but as you move around them, they
turn into another optical illusion (Tribar).
Hence we can say that these sculptures are
'self-referential' illusions: three-dimensional
illusive sculptures, each one including two
other two-dimensional optical illusions!
Bravo, Guido.

# Gallery VI

**Cubamid or pyrube?**
The pyramid-like three-dimensional figure (front and side view) is carved from a cube. But is this solid figure possible?
See page 158

## Tiled Einstein

If you look closely at this image you will see only polygons of different gray hues. Einstein's face was 'tiled' using one of the three regular tessellations composed of regular polygons symmetrically tiling the plane.

**Visual memory test**

Spend a few moments (approximately ten seconds) looking at the graphical representation of a stork in order to memorize it visually. Then close the book, take a pencil and try to reproduce the stork with just one continuous line, without lifting your pencil.

See page 158

### The tribarobolus

The 'tribar thrower' is an early Greek statue. It is also one of the first known three-dimensional representations of an impossible tribar. For those who don't remember, the tribar is apparently a solid object, made of straight beams of square cross-section which join at right angles at the vertices of the triangle they form. Covering up any one corner of this figure makes the three bars appear to be fastened together properly to each other at the other two corners. However, the tribar in its entirety cannot be realized by any three-dimensional object! This illusion depends on 'false perspective', similar to the isometric drawings used in engineering. This sort of baffling object displays an inherent ambiguity of depth.

See page 159

**A baffling structure**
The crowd is attracted by a mysterious, obviously artificial, artifact, maybe from outer space! (More prosaically, it's just an IF – an impossible figure…)

## Deceptive divergent lines

In your opinion, are the lines in the grid perfectly straight and parallel?

See page 159

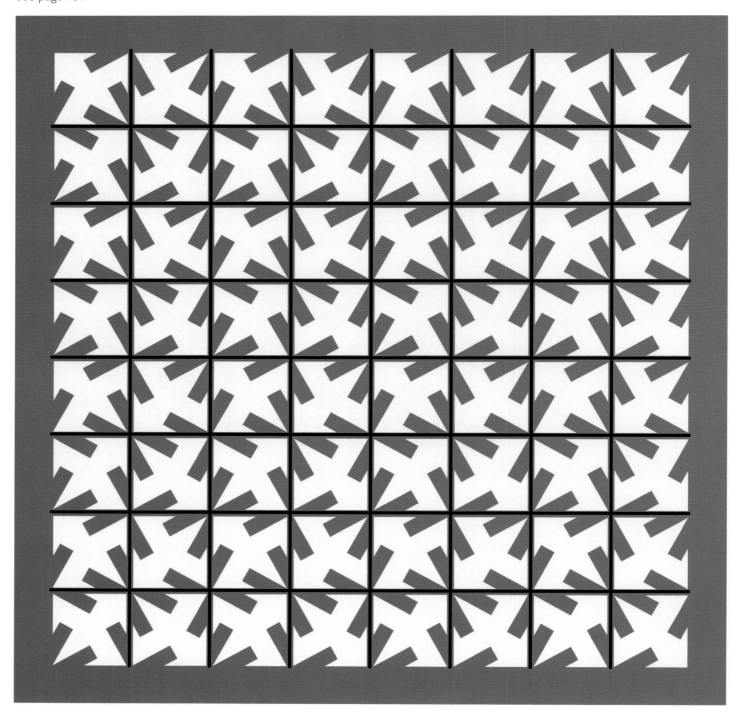

## Challenging squares

Do the green and orange quadrilateral shapes have the same surface?
See page 159

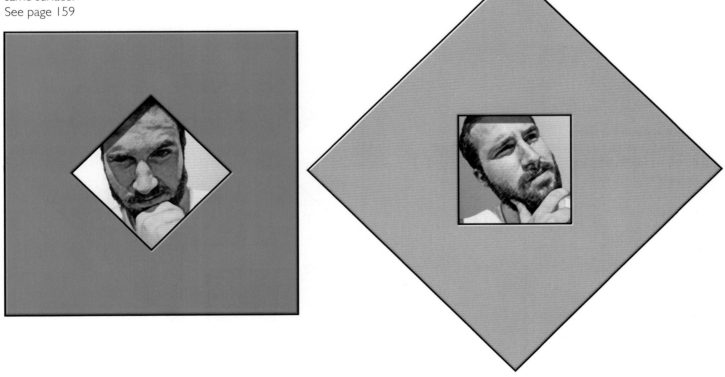

**The mischievous arrows**
Reproduce the three colored arrows, then cut them out in order to form a fourth arrow using all the pieces.
See page 159

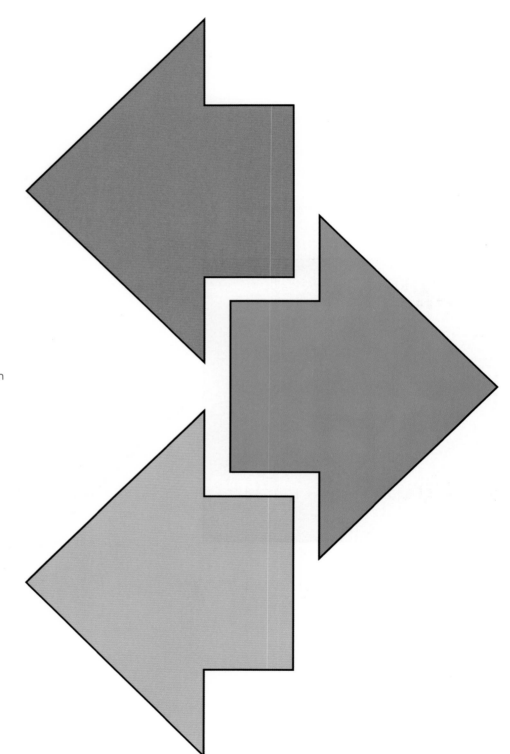

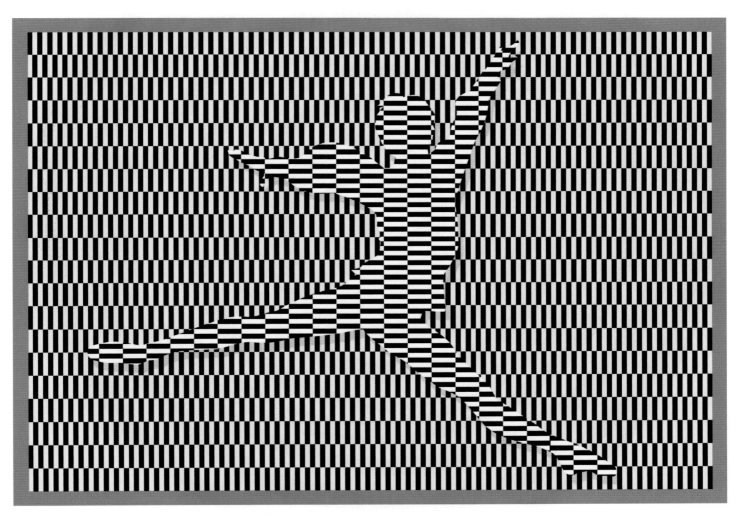

**The dancer**

If you look at the horizontal pattern in the shape representing a dancer, you will probably notice that it appears to move relative to the vertical pattern in the surround. This diagram was adapted from a design created by Japanese artist Hajime Ouchi.
See page 159

**Hypnotic disc**
Observe the disc steadily. How many spirals do
you perceive?
See page 159

**Fish-eye lens effect**
Are the outlines of the squares straight or wavy?
See page 159

**Vibrating squares**

Stare at the picture. Wow! It appears to flicker! Why? Because our eyes are constantly scanning the picture. There are so many lines close together that the eye is unable to make small enough scans to identify the position of individual lines. No matter how hard you try to hold your eye still, it is very exhausting! There is a branch of modern art named Optic Art (or Op Art) which is concerned with such perturbing optic effects.

## Inversion

What do both images have in common? One is the inversion of the other. This kind of interesting distortion, called 'geometric inversion', has the effect of turning the plane inside-out about a given circle. The principle, invented by Jakob Steiner (1793–1863), led to a whole new branch of modern mathematics: projective geometry.

**Swivelling model**
An impossible atomic structure
(hexagonal or cubic?).

## Moiré experiments

When a repeated pattern printed on a transparent acetate sheet is laid over a second one (the background pattern), the combination of both patterns creates a visual interference called 'moiré'. Moirés are also an interesting topic to study and play with! Make a transparent copy of the concentric texture (fig. A) and combine it with its original background to create fascinating moiré effects: by translation (fig. B and C), spatial translation (fig. D) or compression (fig. E). Moiré can also be used to create illusory movements.

**A**

**B**

**C**

**D**

**E**

**Awaiting the impossible**
An impossible tribar in the sky: quick, alert the media!

## Genoese way

Look at this image of a Genoese palazzo (Genoa was the birthplace of Christopher Columbus). The upper and lower sections of the building seem to share a common side, but that is impossible because the image is actually a blending of two different points of view of the same palazzo. The two façades with the portals seem unexpectedly to lean forwards or backwards depending on your angle of view. This illusion, inspired by a photomontage by the artist Coca Frigerio, is comparable to the 'Thiéry figure', a classic ambiguous figure devised by the French psychologist Armand Thiéry in the late 19th century.

**Black and white paradox**

Was the wall black or white? Is there a painter who paints in white, while another paints in black? This shot was taken by the American photographer Mark Chester.

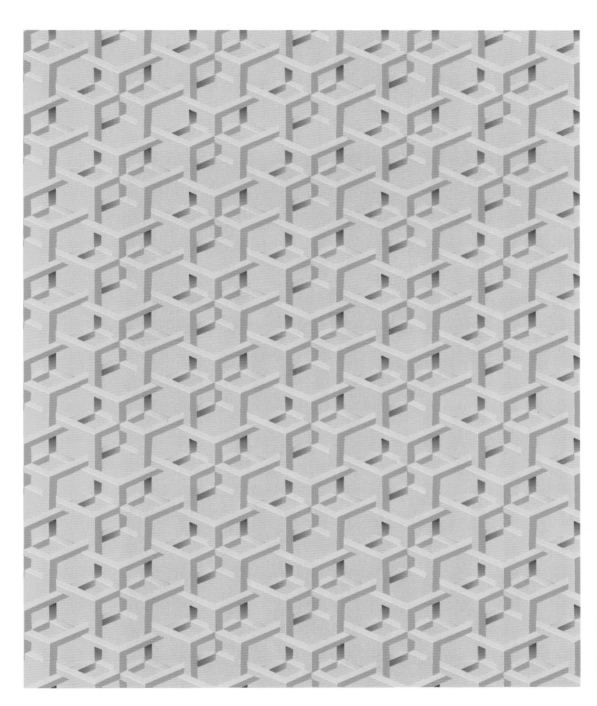

**Improbable interlacing**
Do you perceive any impossible interlaced cubic or hexagonal structure?

## Hidden quadrilaterals

Some squares are camouflaged in this Mexican pattern of white
vertical stripes. Can you spot them?

## Spatial corridor

This is a seemingly three-dimensional picture with the effect of neon colors spreading. The central square seems to glow intensely, but this is just an illusion! The neon color effect was first observed by D. Varin in 1971. The human ability to perceive a neon effect may be a remnant of the development of our power of sight under water at extreme depths, where light is very poor.

**Perpetual vibrations**
The contrasts of the repeated feather-like patterns make the disc vibrate insistently. Your gaze is practically sucked in towards the center of the image! You can use this image to hypnotize your bank manager…

**Neon spreading illusion**
This is a gradient neon spreading illusion.
The border of the central yellow disc
seems to twinkle while the outer disc
appears an even, translucent blue disc
(the white zones between the blue rays
look bluish).

# Gallery VI Solutions

**Visual memory test** (page 137)
See the image. Such a drawing is called in
mathematics a unicursal curve; that is, a
drawing made without lifting your pencil
or crossing a line you have already drawn.
Unicursal drawing is quite simple once you
figure out the trick!

**Cubamid or pyrube?** (page 135)
No, the solids shown in the picture are
actually 'impossible figures'. The illustration
shows how these three-dimensional
objects should in reality appear.

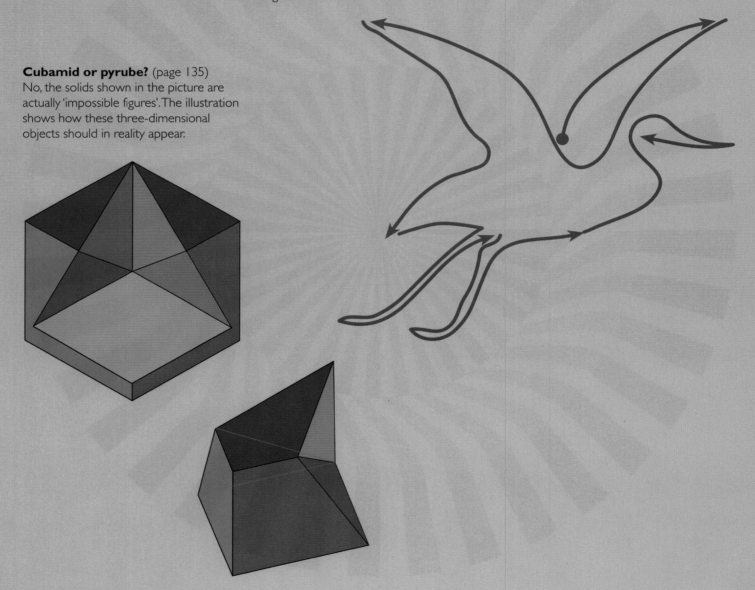